George Richardson **is Chief Examiner and Principal Standards Moderator for Key Skills Application of Number Levels 1-4. He has worked in teaching and as an Educational Advisor for many years and now also edits test papers for Key Skills Application of Number.**

This guide is designed to help students develop the various skills needed in order to pass Key Skills Application of Number Levels 1-3 and Basic Skills Application of Number Levels 1 and 2. It is divided into three sections, one for each level. The first page of each section outlines the requirements on the specification. The rest of the section explores these requirements in greater detail.

Each section includes short tutorials on all the essential number skills, which break calculations down into easy-to-follow steps. Supporting tasks on every page ensure that students can apply what they have learned to practical problems and achieve accurate results.

Key Skills Levels 1 and 2 are tested using multiple choice answer tests. However, the skills and knowledge needed to tackle these questions can only be developed through practice and application, as supported by the tasks in this book. At Levels 1 and 2, calculators are not permitted in the test. Although they can be used for portfolio work, it is recommended that students continue to perform calculations mentally until a process is fully understood.

The Level 3 test requires candidates to demonstrate their skills by completing a series of short practical tasks and one extended question. The use of a scientific calculator is permitted. Candidates should practise using theirs until it becomes a familiar tool.

Candidates at Levels 2 and 3 need to have all the skills from the previous level(s). To ensure that they develop these, candidates should work through each section of the book in turn.

There is a reference section at the back of the book that contains useful information, such as mathematical rules, frequently used formulae and conversion tables.

Contents

You must show that you have developed skills in
- **Interpreting information**
- **Carrying out calculations**
- **Interpreting results and presenting your findings**

The symbols P and T indicate which skills are likely to be required for the portfolio and/or the test.

Ⓟ ... Portfolio
Ⓣ ... Test

Interpreting Information

In interpreting information you need to know how to...

Ⓟ Ⓣ ... read and understand straightforward tables, charts, diagrams and line graphs

Ⓟ Ⓣ ... read and understand numbers used in different ways

Ⓟ Ⓣ ... measure in everyday units by reading scales on familiar measuring equipment

Ⓟ Ⓣ ... make accurate observations

Ⓟ Ⓣ ... identify suitable calculations to get the results you need for your task

Carrying Out Calculations

In carrying out calculations you need to know how to...

Ⓟ Ⓣ ... work to the level of accuracy you have been told to use

Ⓟ Ⓣ ... add, subtract, multiply and divide with whole numbers and simple decimals

Ⓟ Ⓣ ... understand and find simple fractions and percentages

Ⓟ Ⓣ ... work out areas of rectangular spaces

Ⓟ Ⓣ ... work out volumes of rectangular-based shapes

Ⓟ Ⓣ ... use straightforward scales on diagrams

Ⓟ Ⓣ ... use ratios and proportion

Ⓟ Ⓣ ... find the average (mean) of up to 10 items

Ⓟ Ⓣ ... find the range for up to 10 items

Ⓟ Ⓣ ... check calculations using different methods to make sure they make sense

*Sir Isaac Newton
(1642-1727)*

Interpreting Results and Presenting Your Findings

In interpreting results and presenting your findings you need to know how to...

Ⓟ Ⓣ ... use suitable ways of presenting information including a chart and diagram

Ⓟ Ⓣ ... use the correct units

Ⓟ Ⓣ ... label your work correctly

Ⓟ ... describe how the results of your calculations meet the purpose of your task

BASIC NUMBER SKILLS 1

You need to know how to read and understand numbers used in different ways, including large numbers in figures or words, simple fractions, decimals and percentages. You should be able to add, subtract, multiply and divide with whole numbers and simple decimals, and understand and find simple fractions and percentages.

Understanding Large Numbers

How many miles is the moon from Earth? How many seconds are there in one year? Very large numbers like these can be difficult to picture. However, the shape of the written number (rather than the digits themselves) can help you to understand the 'size' of the number. When large numbers are written with the digits arranged in groups of three, the pattern formed shows how large the number is.

EXAMINER'S HINT:

Take a moment to look at these simple numbers. The digits are grouped in threes, with a space between to help you read them. On the left-hand side, it is the position of the '1' that helps you to read the number. The quantity of '0's in it tells you its size.

1	One
10	Ten
100	One hundred
1 000	One thousand
10 000	Ten thousand
100 000	One hundred thousand
1 000 000	One million

You need to be able to change large numbers from figures to words and from words to figures. Once you understand the '3 group' pattern, it is possible to build any number of any size.

110	One hundred and ten
1 100	One thousand, one hundred or eleven hundred
1 001 000	One million and one thousand
1 001 100	One million, one thousand and one hundred
1 010 010	One million, ten thousand and ten
10 000 101	Ten million, one hundred and one
53 604 950 023	Fifty three thousand, six hundred and four million, nine hundred and fifty thousand and twenty three

TASK 1

Use the '3 group' pattern to change the following numbers into figures or words:

EXAMINER'S HINT:

When writing large numbers as words, the spaces between the groups of digits are replaced with 'and' or a comma (,) to make them easier to read and understand.

Figures	Words
34 004 500	
	Forty five million, one thousand and four
940 000 035	
	One hundred and twenty three million, four hundred and fifty six thousand

Place Value

Each digit in a whole number has a place value, for example...

Thousands	Hundreds	Tens	Units	
			8	Eight
		7	4	Seventy four
	3	2	9	Three hundred and twenty nine
4	6	0	5	Four thousand, six hundred and five

EXAMINER'S HINT:

It does not matter how large a number is, each digit will have a place value.

Addition and Subtraction of Whole Numbers

Whenever you add or subtract whole numbers you must line up the digits, one on top of the other, in place value order.

EXAMINER'S HINT:

There are many ways of doing the calculations shown on this page. The methods shown here are typical. However, if you have a different method that always gives you the right answer - stick with it!

It does not matter how many digits you have in your whole numbers - just make sure you line up your numbers in place value order.

EXAMPLES

1 356 + 72

$$356 + {}_1 72 = 428$$

- Start from the right hand side.
- 6 + 2 = 8. Put 8 down.
- 5 + 7 = 12. Put 2 down and carry 1.
- 3 + 1 = 4. Put 4 down.

2 438 - 57

$$438 - 57 = 381$$

- Start from the right hand side.
- 8 - 7 = 1. Put 1 down.
- 3 - 5 doesn't work. Borrow 10 from the next column to give 13 - 5 = 8. Put 8 down.
- 3 - 0 = 3. Put 3 down.

Multiplication and Division of Whole Numbers

EXAMPLES

1 364 x 14

$$
\begin{array}{r}
364 \\
\times \ 14 \\
\hline
3640 \\
1456 \\
\hline
5096
\end{array}
$$

- 14 = 10 + 4.
- Do the 364 x 10 first. Remember to put a '0' down as you would if you multiplied any whole number by 10.
- Do the 364 x 4 multiplication.
- Add the two multiplications together.

2 312 ÷ 12

$$
\begin{array}{r}
26 \\
12\overline{)312} \\
24 \\
\hline
72 \\
72 \\
\hline
0
\end{array}
$$

- 12 does not divide into 3 so move on.
- 12 into 31 goes 2 times. 12 x 2 = 24. Write 24 below 31 and subtract to give 7.
- Bring down the 2. 12 into 72 goes 6 times. 12 x 6 = 72.

EXAMINER'S HINT:

You need to know the multiplication or 'times' tables up to at least 10. Do practise these tables as they are skills you need for life.

TASK 2

Work out the following:

1. 124 + 35
2. 4307 + 245
3. 9093 + 48 + 231
4. 136 – 24
5. 3625 – 475
6. 4821 – 56
7. 32 x 8
8. 133 x 12
9. 4375 x 16
10. 344 ÷ 8
11. 456 ÷ 12
12. 7170 ÷ 15

Understanding Simple Fractions

Pizzas and pies can be shared by cutting them into halves, thirds or quarters. With one, two or three friends, fractions tell you how to share your meal fairly.

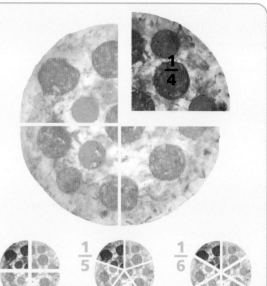

Some friends order a pizza. Four of them want a slice, so they cut the **whole** pizza into **four equal parts** (or slices). Each friend has **one of the four** slices. The 'shorthand' for writing this is:

Each friend has $\frac{1}{4}$ of the pizza.

This shorthand is very flexible. The pizza could have been cut into any number of slices.

Writing Fractions in Chains

You can build chains of equal fractions using any times table. Simply multiply both numbers in the fraction by the same number, for example:

$$\frac{1}{2} \xrightarrow{\times 2} \text{is the same as } \frac{2}{4} \xrightarrow{\times 2} \text{is the same as } \frac{4}{8} \xrightarrow{\times 2} \text{is the same as } \frac{8}{16} \xrightarrow{\times 2} \text{is the same as } \frac{16}{32} \text{ etc.}$$

This chain was formed using the two times table. Another chain of equal fractions could be formed using the three times table.

Multiplying using the three times table $\frac{1}{2} = \frac{3}{6} = \frac{9}{18} = \frac{27}{54} = \frac{81}{162}$ etc.

You can also divide large numbers in a fraction by the same number to make them smaller.

Dividing using the five times table $\frac{25}{125} = \frac{5}{25} = \frac{1}{5}$

Chains of equal fractions that are built using division always have an end; you will reach a point where the numbers cannot be made any smaller.

TASK 3

Multiply using the two, three and five times tables to build three chains for each of the following fractions.

① $\frac{1}{4}$ ② $\frac{1}{3}$ ③ $\frac{3}{4}$ ④ $\frac{2}{3}$ ⑤ $\frac{4}{5}$

Choose a suitable times table and build a chain for each of these fractions using division. Keep going until you reach the end of the chain.

⑥ $\frac{16}{40}$ ⑦ $\frac{60}{120}$ ⑧ $\frac{8}{64}$ ⑨ $\frac{75}{125}$ ⑩ $\frac{9}{63}$

Simplifying Fractions

In one of the chains you have just built you should have found that $\frac{60}{120} = \frac{1}{2}$.
If you think about a pizza, it is much easier to picture $\frac{1}{2}$ than $\frac{60}{120}$.

Whenever you come across a fraction, look to see if you can use your times tables to divide it and make it simpler. Simple fractions are much easier to work with.

Simplifying 'Top Heavy' Fractions

Some fractions are known as **improper** because they are 'top heavy'
i.e. the top number is bigger than the bottom number.

$\frac{5}{4}$ is 'top heavy'. It needs **simplifying** so that it is easier to read and understand.

> **EXAMPLE**
> Look back at the pizza on the facing page.
>
> $\frac{5}{4}$ would be one whole pizza cut into four slices, plus one extra slice from another pizza. In other words:
>
> $$\frac{5}{4} = \frac{4}{4} + \frac{1}{4} = 1\frac{1}{4}$$

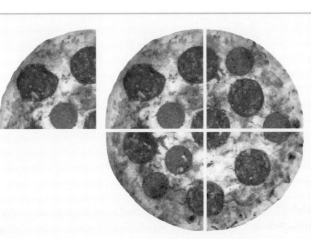

Whenever you are presented with a 'top heavy' fraction, you can convert it into a **whole number and fraction** in this way.

Adding and Subtracting Fractions

Once you know how to make number chains and simplify 'top heavy' fractions, you can add and subtract fractions.

> **EXAMPLES**
>
> **1** $\frac{1}{2} + \frac{2}{3} = ?$
>
> $\frac{1}{2} + \frac{2}{3} = \frac{3}{6} + \frac{4}{6} = ?$ The first step is to build chains and change the fractions so that the bottom numbers in the sum are all the same.
>
> $\frac{1}{2} + \frac{2}{3} = \frac{3}{6} + \frac{4}{6} = \frac{7}{6} = 1\frac{1}{6}$ Now, add the top numbers together and simplify the answer if necessary.
>
> **2** $\frac{4}{5} - \frac{3}{4} = \frac{16}{20} - \frac{15}{20} = \frac{1}{20}$ The same steps can be followed when subtracting fractions.

EXAMINER'S HINT:

You are in control of the numbers - build new fraction chains to help you with your calculations as and when you need to. You are unlikely to need more than your 2, 3 or 5 times tables to build chains.

EXAMINER'S HINT:

It often helps to read what you have written aloud.
e.g. three sixths plus four sixths equals seven sixths. NOT seven twelfths!

TASK 4

Use chains and your simplifying skills to solve these:

1 $\frac{1}{4} + \frac{1}{2}$ **2** $\frac{3}{4} - \frac{1}{2}$ **3** $\frac{1}{3} + \frac{1}{5}$ **4** $\frac{3}{4} - \frac{1}{5}$ **5** $\frac{5}{6} - \frac{3}{5}$

Understanding Simple Decimals

When you use money and metric measures, such as millimetres, litres or grams, you often use simple decimals, so it is a good idea to be confident with this type of number. Fortunately, decimals are an easy kind of fraction - easy because the ten times table is the only one ever needed! If you remember your pizza, with decimals the whole pizza is only ever divided into ten, one hundred or one thousand slices.

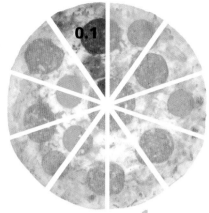

where each slice $= \dfrac{1}{10}$ or **0.1**

 0.1   0.2   0.3   0.4   0.5

The table below shows the relationship between decimals and fractions:

Decimal Number	Place Value of Digits					
	10 Tens	1 Units	• DECIMAL POINT	$\frac{1}{10}$ Tenths	$\frac{1}{100}$ Hundredths	$\frac{1}{1\,000}$ Thousandths
0.03		0		0	3	
0.005		0		0	0	5
26.75	2	6		7	5	
0.24		0		2	4	

e.g. **0.03** is $\dfrac{3}{100}$ or three hundredths

EXAMINER'S HINT:

Return to this place value table to remind yourself if you ever get stuck working with decimals. When you read decimal numbers as they appear e.g. 0.005 as 'zero point zero zero five', it is easy to forget what the figures represent.

The **position** of the decimal point is just as important as the digits themselves. It may seem like a small mistake, but if you misplace the decimal point it makes a huge difference because all the place values change. For example, baked beans cost £0.23 a can. However, if the shopkeeper makes a mistake when pricing his stock and labels them £2.30, no one will ever buy them!

TASK 5

Complete the place value table below by filling in the missing decimals and digits.

Decimal Number	Place Value of Digits					
	10 Tens	1 Units	• DECIMAL POINT	$\frac{1}{10}$ Tenths	$\frac{1}{100}$ Hundredths	$\frac{1}{1\,000}$ Thousandths
		0		4		
0.05						
		6		0	0	9
50.078						

Calculating with Decimals

If you can add and subtract whole numbers, you can do the same with decimals. The most important thing to remember is to arrange the numbers on top of each other so that the digits with the same place value are in columns. The easiest way to do this is to line up the decimal points.

EXAMPLES

① 2.9 + 0.67

$$\begin{array}{r} 2.90 \\ +\ 0.67 \\ \hline 3.57 \end{array}$$

Remember to bring the decimal point down to your answer!

② 3.8 - 0.67

$$\begin{array}{r} 3.\overset{7}{8}\overset{1}{0} \\ -\ 0.67 \\ \hline 3.13 \end{array}$$

Remember to take the decimal point down to your answer!

When multiplying or dividing decimals, set the calculations out in exactly the same way as you would for whole numbers.

EXAMPLES

① 12.6 x 14

$$\begin{array}{r} 12.6 \\ \times\quad 14 \\ \hline 126.0 \\ 50.4 \\ \hline 176.4 \end{array}$$

When **multiplying** remember to bring the decimal point **down** to your answer.

② 13.2 ÷ 6

$$\begin{array}{r} 2.2 \\ 6\overline{)13.2} \\ 12\downarrow \\ \hline 12 \\ 12 \\ \hline 0 \end{array}$$

When **dividing** remember to take the decimal point **up** to your answer.

TASK 6

Answer the following questions, setting them out carefully to help your calculations.

① 3.6 + 7.9   **②** 7.9 - 3.6   **③** 13.2 + 8.3 + 9.6   **④** 11.1 - 3.04
⑤ 45.45 x 4   **⑥** 22.4 ÷ 4   **⑦** 31.3 x 12   **⑧** 72.63 ÷ 9

Understanding Money

Amounts of money (e.g. prices) are frequently written as decimals. The amount in pounds appears in front of the decimal point and the amount in pence appears after the decimal point.

EXAMPLES

Ninety nine pence = £0.99	Six pounds and one penny = £6.01
Three pounds fifty = £3.50	One penny = £0.01

You add, subtract, multiply and divide money in exactly the same way as decimals.

EXAMINER'S HINT:

You can fill in zeros instead of leaving gaps if you find it helps.

EXAMINER'S HINT:

To multiply two decimals, ignore the decimal points and multiply as you would whole numbers. You can put the decimal point in at the end. In your answer, the number of digits after the decimal point should be the same as the **total** number of digits after the decimal points in the numbers being multiplied.

e.g. $10.\overset{\frown}{2}$ x $4.\overset{\frown}{6}$ = $46.\overset{\frown}{9}\overset{\frown}{2}$

$\quad 4.\overset{\frown}{3}\overset{\frown}{2}$ x $15.\overset{\frown}{1}$ = $65.\overset{\frown}{2}\overset{\frown}{3}\overset{\frown}{2}$

To multiply a decimal by 10, 100, 1000 all you have to do is move your decimal point a certain number of places to the right.
e.g. 4.7423 x 10 = 47.423
4.7423 x 100 = 474.23
4.7423 x 1000= 4742.3

To divide a decimal by 10, 100, 1000 you do the opposite and move your decimal point a certain number of places to the left.
e.g. 4.74 ÷ 10 = 0.474
4.74 ÷ 100 = 0.0474
4.74 ÷ 1000 = 0.00474

EXAMINER'S HINT:

There is 100 pence in one pound, so money is only ever written to two decimal places (showing tenths and hundredths).

BASIC NUMBER SKILLS 4

Understanding Simple Percentages

Percentages are used in everyday life, from pay rises to price reductions. This helps us to make easy comparisons. When you understand the basics of percentages they are even easier than decimals or fractions. They focus on a **whole being equal to one hundred** i.e. the **whole is one hundred percent**. When you have fifty percent of your pizza - you have fifty of the one hundred parts that make up the whole.

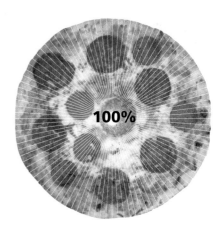
100%

10%   20%   30%   40%   50%

Equivalent Fractions, Decimals and Percentages

Each column in the table below shows the same number expressed as a fraction, decimal and a percentage.

Fraction	$\frac{1}{10}$	$\frac{1}{5}$	$\frac{1}{4}$	$\frac{1}{3}$	$\frac{1}{2}$
Decimal	0.1	0.2	0.25	0.33̇	0.5
Percentage	10%	20%	25%	33.33̇%	50%

EXAMPLE

$\frac{3}{5}$ of the CDs in Peter's collection are pop music. Is this more or less than 55% of his collection? Explain your answer.

From the table above $\frac{1}{5} = 20\%$

Therefore $\frac{3}{5} = 3 \times \frac{1}{5} = 3 \times 20\% = 60\%$

60% is greater than 55%
and so $\frac{3}{5}$ **of his collection is greater than 55% of his collection.**

TASK 7
What are the equivalent...
1 ... decimals and percentages of the following fractions? $\frac{2}{5}$, $\frac{3}{5}$, $\frac{9}{10}$
2 ... fractions and percentages of the following decimals? 0.8, 0.6̇6̇, 0.75
3 ... fractions and decimals of the following percentages? 35%, 70%, 100%

TASK 8
70% of the residents of a street drive a car. Is this more or less than $\frac{2}{3}$ of the residents? Explain your answer.

Calculations Involving Percentages

EXAMPLE
Mary earns £4.80 per hour. She is given a pay rise of 10%. How much will Mary now earn per hour?

Mary's pay rise is 10% of the whole 100%, which is £4.80.

10% is 10 parts out of a 100 parts = $\dfrac{10}{100}$ = $\dfrac{1}{10}$

Her pay rise is therefore $\dfrac{1}{10}$ of £4.80 or $\dfrac{1}{10}$ of 480p.

$$\dfrac{1}{10} \times \dfrac{480}{1} = \dfrac{1 \times 480}{10 \times 1} = \dfrac{480}{10} = 48 \text{ pence}$$

Mary will now earn £4.80 + £0.48 = £5.28 per hour.

EXAMINER'S HINT:
Knowing what the whole is, and that it is equal to 100%, is the key to understanding and using percentages effectively.

TASK 9
Work out the following:
1. ... You normally earn £12 per hour and you receive a 10% pay rise. How much is your pay rise? How much do you now earn per hour?
2. ... What is 75% of a takeaway bill that is £12 in total?
3. ... What is a 45% reduction on a coat that costs £50?
4. ... A new car that normally costs £12 000 is for sale with a 5% reduction. What is the cost of the car?

EXAMPLE
A bakery sold 120 loaves in one afternoon of which 90 were white. What percentage of the loaves sold were white?

120 loaves is equal to the whole 100%

90 loaves is therefore equal to $\dfrac{90}{120}$ of the whole 100%

$$\dfrac{90}{120} \times \dfrac{100}{1}\,\% = \dfrac{90 \times 100}{120 \times 1}\,\% = \dfrac{9000}{120}\,\% = 75\%$$

Therefore 75% of the loaves sold are white.

EXAMINER'S HINT:
You can use a calculator to work out percentages for your portfolio evidence, but make certain that you can do them without a calculator for the test. Whether you are working with or without a calculator you need to know what the **whole 100%** is every time.

TASK 10
Work out the following:
1. ... You normally earn £10 an hour and you receive a £5 an hour pay rise. What is this pay rise as a percentage of your normal earnings?
2. ... A person that weighs 250 kilograms loses 25 kilograms of their weight on a diet. What is this weight loss as a percentage of their original weight?
3. ... A person that weighs 200 kilograms puts on a further 50 kilograms. What is this weight gain as a percentage of their original weight?
4. ... During the course of a day a shop sells 55 tins of baked beans, 36 tins of spaghetti hoops and 29 tins of pasta shapes in a tomato sauce. What percentage of the tins sold were spaghetti hoops?

> You need to know how to make accurate observations and to measure in everyday units by reading scales on familiar measuring equipment using the correct units.

Making Accurate Observation

Making accurate observations is a basic skill. So basic that it is easy to become over confident and make silly mistakes. The following task is set out like a basic or key skills test question. Choose which of the four options is correct.

Count the number of 'f's in the passage below.

Making accurate observations is an application of number skill that is useful for all of us. We can use the skill frequently for a range of different and useful purposes.

A 7   **B** 8   **C** 9   **D** 10

There are ten 'f's in the passage. **The correct answer is D.** However, you may have come up with any one of the alternative answers. There is a certain logic behind them all.

- If you answered A, you probably missed all the 'f's in the 'of's.
- If you answered B, you probably missed all the 'f's in the 'for's.
- If you answered C, you overlooked just one 'f'.

This is not a trick question, but it will catch you out if you are not thorough and accurate in all your work.

TASK 1

Look carefully at the five dogs below. Which one is the odd one out?

Using Familiar Measuring Equipment

Think about the everyday measuring instruments you use to ensure that your day runs smoothly. You might time your egg with the kitchen **clock** at breakfast time; check the **scales** at the supermarket to ensure you buy enough cheese; check the **fuel gauge** in the car to make sure you have enough petrol for a journey ...

TASK 2
List three everyday measuring instruments the following people might use:
1. ... Housewife
2. ... Builder
3. ... Soldier
4. ... Car mechanic
5. ... Nurse

EXAMINER'S HINT:

Take notice of the measuring instruments you come across everyday e.g. measuring jug, thermometer, fuel gauge. Look at them carefully and make sure you know how to read them.

Measuring in Everyday Units

To make sense of the scale on a piece of measuring equipment, you need to know the unit of measurement that is being used. This will depend on what you are measuring:

Metric Units of Measurement				
Length	millimetre mm	centimetre cm (=10mm)	metre m (=100cm)	kilometre km (=1000m)
Mass (Weight)	milligram mg	centigram cg (=10mg)	gram g (=1000mg)	kilogram kg (=1000g)
Volume/Capacity	millilitre ml	centilitre cl (=10ml)	litre l (=1000ml)	
	cubic millimetre mm³	cubic centimetre cm³	cubic metre m³	
Temperature		Celsius °C		

EXAMINER'S HINT:

The most commonly used units of measurement are **Metric** (shown alongside). However, you will also come across **Imperial** units of measurement (e.g. in the UK we use miles to measure journey distances) so you need to be familiar with these too:

- **LENGTH:**
  inch, foot, yard, mile

- **MASS (WEIGHT):**
  ounce, pound

- **CAPACITY:**
  pint, gallon

- **TEMPERATURE:**
  Fahrenheit

TASK 3
1. ... Name three metric and three imperial units for measuring length.
2. ... What is the imperial equivalent of the metric unit gram?
3. ... What is the metric equivalent of the imperial unit Fahrenheit.
4. ... Apart from journey distances in miles, name four other measurements where imperial units are commonly used.

Converting Within the Same System

EXAMPLES

1 Convert 0.2 hours into minutes.
We know that 1 hour = 60 minutes
Therefore 0.2 hours = 0.2 x 60 minutes = 12 minutes

2 Convert 600m into kilometres.
We know that 1000 metres = 1 kilometre (see table from previous page)

Therefore 600 metres = $\frac{600}{1000}$ kilometres = 0.6 kilometres

(see table from previous page)

EXAMINER'S HINT:

A simple way to know if you should multiply or divide to find the final answer is as follows: In Example 1, we know that 1 hour = 60 minutes. As we are going from a smaller number (1) to a bigger number (60), we MULTIPLY. In Example 2, we are going from a bigger number (1000) to a smaller number (1), so we DIVIDE.

TASK 4

1 Convert 2.2kg into grams
2 Convert 1.2m into millimetres
3 Convert 450cm into metres
4 Convert 2.4 hours into minutes
5 Convert 80 minutes into hours and minutes
6 Convert $4\frac{1}{2}$ minutes into seconds

Reading Scales

Most scales use simple count patterns based upon the two, four, five or ten times tables and the basic rules for decimals and fractions. Once you have identified the count pattern, you can take a reading on any straight, vertical or curved scale. Look at the different count patterns on the scales below.

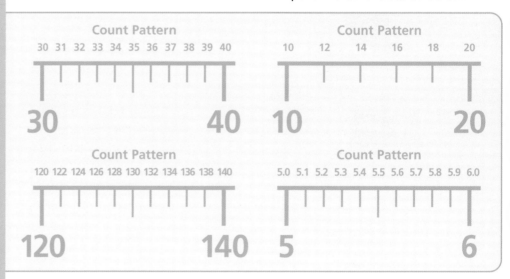

TASK 5

What is the reading given by the pointer on the following scales?

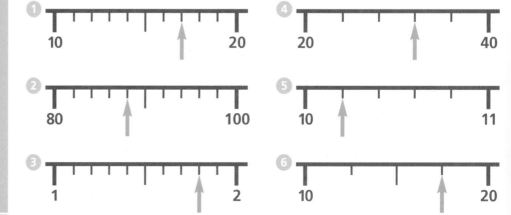

EXAMINER'S HINT:

Before you attempt to answer **TASK 5** make sure that you have correctly identified the count pattern for each scale.

TASK 6

1. What is the reading on the thermometer?

2. A car tyre needs a pressure of 35psi. The pressure gauge shows the pressure in the tyre now. How many more psi are needed in the tyre?

3. Look at the time shown on the alarm clock. You have to get up at eight o'clock. How much longer can you stay in bed?

4. Fresh fruit juice is collected in a jug. How much juice is in the measuring jug?

5. This picture shows the time on your kitchen clock. Your favourite soap starts at 20.30. How many minutes are there before the programme starts?

AREA AND VOLUME

You should be able to work out areas of rectangular spaces and the volumes of rectangular-based shapes, using the correct units.

Calculating Areas

How often, after decorating, are you left with spare rolls of wallpaper, tiles or tins of paint? Wastage like this can be reduced if you calculate the **area** (size) of the surface to be decorated before you begin.

EXAMPLE
You want to carpet your bedroom floor. Before you buy any carpet you will need to calculate the area of the floor. This is a simple calculation, providing you follow these four easy steps:

1. Measure the length and width of the floor using a tape measure.
2. Draw a basic diagram of the floor and mark on the two measurements.
3. Divide the diagram into '**metre squares**' (because metres were the units used to measure the length and width).
4. Now count how many 'metre squares' cover the floor's surface...

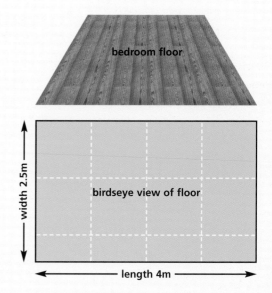

There are 8 whole 'metre squares' and 4 half 'metre squares'. Therefore, in total there are:

$$8 + \frac{1}{2} + \frac{1}{2} + \frac{1}{2} + \frac{1}{2} = 8 + \frac{4}{2} = 10 \text{ 'metre squares'}$$

These 'metre squares' are written as **square metres** or **m²** so, the total **area** of the floor is written as **10m²**.

If the length and width of the floor had been measured in **centimetres**, then the floor would be divided into 'centimetre squares' and the area would be written as **square centimetres** or **cm²**.

TASK 1
Calculate the area of the following surfaces by drawing a diagram and counting the number of unit squares:
1. ... a garden wall that is 1.5m high and 20m long.
2. ... a garage floor that is 2.5m wide and 7m long.
3. ... a tile that is 10cm long and 10cm wide.
4. ... a roof that is 8.5m long and 3.5m wide.

Calculating Volumes

Once you can calculate the area of rectangles, you can go one step further and work out the **volume** of rectangular-based shapes (e.g. boxes). Volume is the amount of space taken up by a three-dimensional shape.

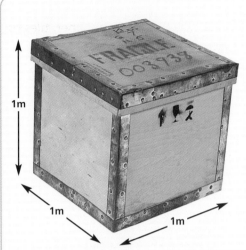

EXAMPLE

You hire a lorry to help you move house and want to calculate the total volume of the load it can carry. The lorry's container is 3 metres high, 2 metres wide and 4 metres long. All your packing boxes are 1 metre high, 1 metre wide and 1 metre long.

Each box has sides that are all of equal length (1m), so it is **cube shaped**. The volume of one box is **1 metre cubed** or **1m³**.

To work out the total volume of the lorry, all we have to do is calculate how many 1m³ boxes it can carry. To do this we can:
1. Draw a basic diagram of the lorry container and mark on its measurements.
2. Divide the diagram into '**metre cubes**'.

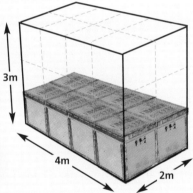

You can see that a single layer of boxes is 4 boxes long and 2 boxes wide.

4 boxes x **2** boxes = **8** boxes

The container is 3 metres high, so you can fit 3 layers of 1m tall boxes into it.

3 layers x **8** boxes = **24** boxes

Because we know each box has a volume of 1m³, we can conclude that the total **volume** of the load that the lorry can carry in its container is **24m³**.

EXAMINER'S HINT:

It is important to always use the correct units. The units used for measuring length will determine the units that you use for area and volume.

	length	area	volume
centimetres	cm	cm²	cm³
metres	m	m²	m³
kilometres	km	km²	km³

EXAMINER'S HINT:

Always draw on the diagram to show how many boxes are in each layer and how many layers there are.

EXAMINER'S HINT:

The lorry is 3m high by 4m long by 2m wide. Its total volume is 24m³. This can be summarised in a simple equation:

3 x 4 x 2 = 24m³

HEIGHT X LENGTH X WIDTH = VOLUME

This is the standard formula used for calculating the volume of rectangular based shapes. Use this formula to check your answers for Task 2.

TASK 2

1. ... Draw a diagram to calculate the number of 1cm³ sugar cubes in an unopened box that is 10cm long, 8cm wide and 6cm high. What is the volume of sugar in the box?

2. ... Draw a diagram to calculate the number of 1m³ cases on a pallet that is 2m wide and 2m long, when the cases are stacked three high. What is the total volume of the boxes on the pallet?

> **You need to know how to use ratios and proportion.**

Ratio and proportion can be very useful when preparing food. How much rice do you need to boil? How many tea bags are needed to make a pot of tea? How much bread is needed for a meal? There is no fixed answer to any of these questions because each depends upon the size (weight, volume, length) of what you are preparing. How many people want rice? How many cups of tea are needed from the tea pot? How long is the french stick? Weight, volume and length can be judged from experience but, when you need to be more accurate, ratio and proportion can help.

Using Proportion

EXAMINER'S HINT:

Start by finding out how many servings of rice you can make with **one** cup of water. Once you know this, the other calculations will be easy.

EXAMPLE
This recipe for Boiled Rice, taken from the Internet, makes four servings:

How many cups of water do you need to make 6 servings of rice?
The same method used to make chains of fractions can be applied to scale and proportion. When it is set out in a simple, logical form it is easy:
- From the recipe we know that: **2 cups** of water makes **4 servings**.
- Which also means that: **4 servings** need **2 cups** of water.

We can make a chain of equal proportions just like we made a chain of equal fractions, by using the two, three or five times tables.

If	**4 servings**		need		**2 cups** of water
Then	**2 servings**	÷2	need	÷2	**1 cup** of water
And	**6 servings**	x3	need	x3	**3 cups** of water

EXAMINER'S HINT:

Remember, you are in control. Take the information you have been given and set it out in a way that makes it easy for you to use:
- 2 cups of water makes 4 servings
It is logical to turn this around ...
- 4 servings need 2 cups of water
... so that the information you are looking for comes at the end.

TASK 1
1 ... Develop the chain of equal proportion above to work out how many cups of water you need to make: 12 servings; 20 servings.
2 ... Make a new chain of equal proportions to work out how much rice you need for 20 servings; 12 servings; 1 serving.

Using Ratio

Ratio shows the relationship in quantity between one thing and another.

EXAMPLE

For breakfast a man decides to make a fresh fruit smoothie. He uses one banana and five strawberries. The ratio of the number of bananas to strawberries can be written as **1 to 5** or **1:5**. He decides to make a large quantity of fruit smoothie and store some in the fridge. If he uses three bananas, how many strawberries will he need?

The ratio of bananas to strawberries needed to make the smoothie is **1:5**. In other words, for every banana, five strawberries are needed.

Therefore, if he uses **3** bananas he needs...
3 x 5 =15 strawberries.

EXAMINER'S HINT:

The numbers in a ratio always follow the same order as the items in the written statement e.g. If the ratio of bananas to strawberries is 1:5, the ratio of strawberries to bananas is 5:1.

TASK 2

1 ... If you have 7 bananas how many strawberries do you need to make the smoothie?

2 ... If you have 25 strawberries how many bananas do you need?

EXAMPLES

1 One hundred guests are invited to a wedding. Sixty of the guests are women. What is the ratio of women to men?

If **60** of the guests are women, the remaining **40** must be men. Therefore, the ratio of women to men is ...

$$60:40 = \frac{60}{10}:\frac{40}{10} = 6:4 = \frac{6}{2}:\frac{4}{2} = 3:2$$

(divide both figures by 10)   (divide both figures by 2)

EXAMINER'S HINT:

Ratios can be simplified in exactly the same way as fractions.

2 If **60** guests are invited to the wedding reception and the ratio of women to men is **2:1**, how many guests are women?

The numbers in the ratio represent parts of the whole. To find out how many parts make up the whole you simply add the numbers in the ratio together.

There are **60** guests in total. This is the whole. The ratio of women to men is **2:1**, therefore the whole is divided into **2 + 1 = 3 parts.**

$$\text{The value of 1 part is ...} \quad \frac{\text{whole}}{\text{number of parts}} = \frac{60}{3} = 20 \text{ guests}$$

EXAMINER'S HINT:

Two of three parts are women. This could also be written as the fraction $\frac{2}{3}$.

Two of the three parts are women, so the number of guests that are women is **2 x 20 = 40.**

TASK 3

If fifty people visit the local swimming pool and the ratio of adults to children is 4:1, how many children visit the swimming pool?

> You should be able to read and understand tables, charts, diagrams and line graphs and use straightforward scales on diagrams. You also need to know how to use suitable ways of presenting information, including a chart or diagram, and label your work correctly.

Information can often be presented in tables, charts, diagrams and line graphs to provide a visual picture of what is happening.

Understanding the Visual Picture

EXAMINER'S HINT:

Always approach a chart, graph or pictogram in the same way:

Look at the visual picture, then... read around the picture.

Remember to look for:
- A Title
- Labels
- A Key/Units

Graphs and charts are meaningless without them. Always make sure you include a title and labels when you draw your own.

When you are presented with a table, chart, diagram or graph you need to look closely at the **visual picture**. Can you see a pattern? To help make sense of what you are seeing, you will then need to **read around the picture**. Look for...
- A Title
- Labels
- A Key or Units

Piece all this information together and the overall picture will make sense. Tables, charts, diagrams and graphs all show information in different ways. When you know the basic advantages and disadvantages of each, they are easier to use and understand.

	ADVANTAGE	DISADVANTAGE
Table	All related information is gathered together in one place. This format makes it easy to find specific information.	Where there are lots of numbers it is difficult to see any pattern.
Pie Chart	It is easy to see and compare the largest and smallest sector (slice) etc.	Becomes complicated when there are lots of sectors. It can be difficult to calculate the size of sectors when drawing one.
Bar Chart	Data can be represented accurately. They can also be used to provide comparisons between two (or more) sets of data.	Can only be used to show discrete data (see next page).
Line Graph	Provides a continuous picture of change.	Line graphs are often used incorrectly and the accuracy of readings for 'in between' values cannot be guaranteed!

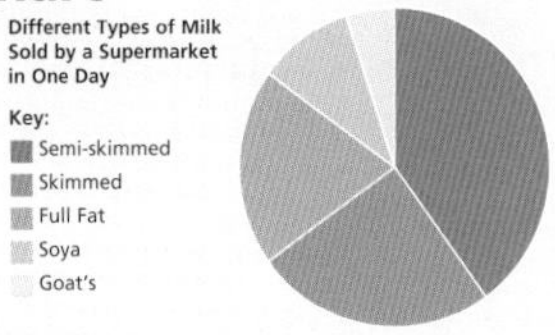

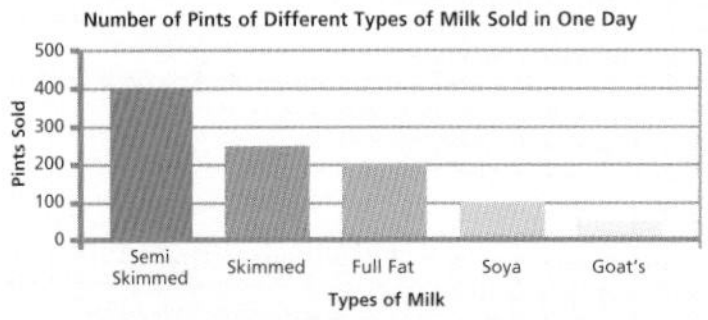

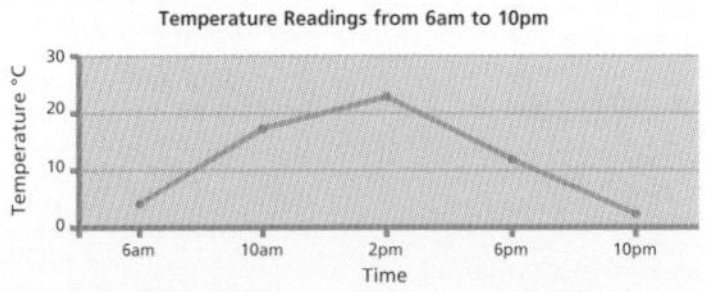

TASK 1

Look at the table above. Which type of diagram (table, pie chart, bar chart, line graph) would be best suited to show...

1. ... the departure and arrival times of the Number 72 bus?
2. ... the number of students who scored A, B and C grades in a test?
3. ... temperature measurements taken in a garden at regular intervals throughout the day?

Tables

Shop Opening Hours

	Morning	Afternoon
Monday	9.30 - 12.00	1.30 - 5.30
Tuesday	8.00 - 12.00	1.30 - 5.30
Wednesday	8.00 - 12.00	Closed
Thursday	8.00 - 12.00	1.30 - 6.30
Friday	8.00 - 12.00	1.30 - 7.30
Saturday	7.30 - 12.00	1.00 - 4.00
Sunday	Closed	Closed

This table shows the opening hours for a small shop. This kind of table appears on the doors of most shops. It gives a lot of detailed information in a clear visual format. A shopper can easily find out when the shop opens, how many hours it is open on any day etc.

TASK 2

1 ... On which day is the shop open longest?

2 ... Is the shop open for longer on Monday or Saturday?

3 ... How many hours in total does the shop open for in one week?

Bar Charts

Number of Pints of Different Types of Milk Sold in One Day

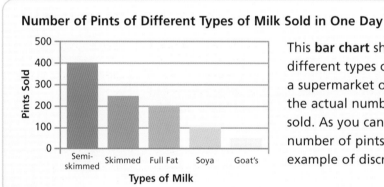

This **bar chart** shows the different types of milk sold in a supermarket on one day and the actual number of pints sold. As you can see, the number of pints sold is an example of discrete data.

TASK 3

1 ... What is the most popular type of milk and how many pints are sold?

2 ... How much soya milk does the supermarket sell?

Bar charts can also be used to compare two or more related sets of data.

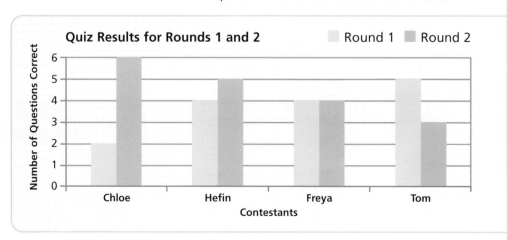

TASK 4

1 ... Who won Round 1 and how many questions did they answer correctly?

2 ... Which contestants had the same overall score?

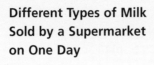

Pie Charts

Different Types of Milk Sold by a Supermarket on One Day

Key:
- Semi-skimmed
- Skimmed
- Full Fat
- Soya
- Goat's

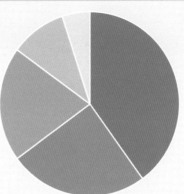

This **pie chart** shows similar information to the bar chart on the previous page. However, where the bar chart shows the actual number of pints sold, the pie chart shows the proportion of different types of milk sold by a supermarket on one day.

Pie charts are useful for comparing different quantities at a glance. There is a sector (slice) for each different type of milk. For each type of milk, the size of its sector represents the amount sold by that supermarket as a **percentage** of all the milk sold in one day.

TASK 5

1 ... What is the most popular type of milk sold?
2 ... What is the least popular type of milk sold?
3 ... Does the shop sell more goat's milk or soya milk?

Pictograms

Rainy Days: July–December 2003

July	🌧️ 🌧️ 🌧️
August	🌧️ 🌧️ 🌧️ 🌧️
September	🌧️ 🌧️ 🌧️
October	🌧️ 🌧️ 🌧️
November	🌧️ 🌧️ 🌧️ 🌧️ 🌧️
December	🌧️ 🌧️ 🌧️ 🌧️ 🌧️

A pictogram uses a symbol or image to represent data.

What visual picture does this pictogram give?

There are more rain symbols at the bottom of the pictogram than at the top.

2 rainy days =

Reading around the picture will provide further information:
- **The Title** tells you that the pictogram shows how many rainy days there were in the last half of 2003.
- **The Key** tells you that each 🌧️ symbol represents 2 rainy days.
- **The Labels** tell you that the data (the number of rainy days) has been grouped into individual months.

TASK 6

1 ... Which was the wettest month in the last six months of 2003?
2 ... How many rainy days were there in August?
3 ... Which two months had the same number of rainy days?

Line Graphs

Line Graphs are used to show a continuous picture of change in data, which is usually collected by taking some sort of measurement. If you plot these measurements on a graph and join them together with a line, the line shows what the 'in between values' are likely to be.

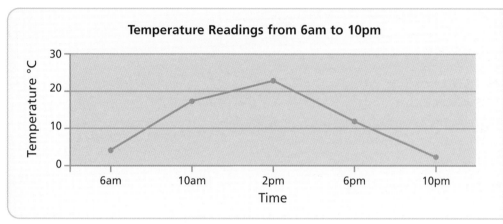

Temperature Readings from 6am to 10pm

EXAMINER'S HINT:

The **axes** of a chart or graph are the two reference lines that form its 'frame'. The line which runs from left to right (horizontally) is called the **x axis**. The line which runs from bottom to top (vertically) is called the **y axis**.

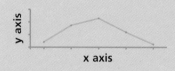

TASK 7

1 ... At what time was the highest temperature reading taken?
2 ... Between which two times was there the least change in temperature?
3 ... Between which two times was there the greatest change in temperature?

Drawing Diagrams to Scale

EXAMPLE

The diagram shows a plot of land. If the scale of the drawing is 1cm represents 2m, what is the length and width of the plot?

All you have to do is measure, using a ruler, the length and width and then convert these measurements into metres.

Length of plot = 6cm
Therefore actual length
$$= 6 \times 2m = 12m$$

Width of plot = 3.5cm
Therefore actual width
$$= 3.5 \times 2m = 7m$$

TASK 8

The scale diagrams below show two plots of land. For each plot calculate the total length of its boundary.

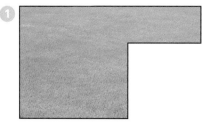

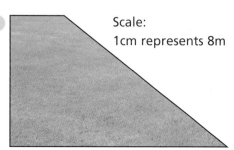

Scale:
1cm represents 8m

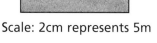
Scale: 2cm represents 5m

EXAMINER'S HINT:

In the test, you are told when a diagram is drawn to scale. Do not assume a diagram is to scale otherwise.

> You should be able to find the range and average (mean) for up to 10 items.

Range

The **range** is the difference between the largest value and the smallest value in a set of data.

$$\text{RANGE} = \text{LARGEST VALUE} - \text{SMALLEST VALUE}$$

EXAMPLE

The weights of six people are as follows: 64kg, 81kg, 73kg, 62kg, 84kg, 70kg. What is the range of their weights?

If you look at the data you will notice that:
The largest value = 84kg
The smallest value = 62kg

RANGE = Largest Value - Smallest Value

$$= 84_{kg} - 62_{kg} = 22_{kg}$$

TASK 1

Calculate the range of the following sets of data:

1. ... £15, £4, £36, £18, £9, £3, £50, £47.
2. ... 420km, 160km, 300km, 100km, 350km, 600km.

Average (Mean)

The **average** or **mean** of a set of data is given by:

$$\text{AVERAGE (MEAN)} = \frac{\text{TOTAL OF ALL THE VALUES}}{\text{NUMBER OF VALUES}}$$

In other words, you add up all the values given and then divide this total by the number of values.

EXAMPLE

The age (in years) of five people travelling in a car is as follows: 18, 46, 5, 43, 23. What is the average age of the people in the car?

$$\text{AVERAGE (MEAN)} = \frac{\text{Total of all the Values}}{\text{Number of Values}}$$

$$= \frac{18 + 46 + 5 + 43 + 23}{5} = \frac{135}{5} = 27_{years}$$

TASK 2

Calculate the average (mean) of the following sets of data:

1. ... 16cm, 8cm, 4cm, 3cm, 14cm.
2. ... 56kg, 70kg, 31kg, 42kg, 35kg, 36kg.

So far we have found the range and average (mean) of straightforward sets of data. The example that follows shows a table of results where there is a variety of possible calculations of range and average. This sort of table is typical of the evidence you could include in your portfolio, as in many cases the calculations involved require a calculator.

EXAMPLE

The table below shows the hours worked by different members of staff at a supermarket. Calculate the range and average (mean) of the number of part-time staff that work at the supermarket each day.

Number of hours worked by staff at the supermarket

		Mon	Tues	Wed	Thurs	Fri	Sat	Sun
Full-time	Manager	8	4	0	8	8	8	4
	Assistant Manager	6	8	0	8	6	4	8
	Assistant Manager	6	0	8	8	6	8	4
	Office Manager	6	0	6	6	6	6	2
Part-time	Hassan	0	0	2	3	7	8	0
	Emil	6	0	0	0	0	0	6
	Petra	3	0	0	0	0	4	3
	John	0	2	2	0	2	5	3
	Jo	0	0	2	0	2	3	5
	Luke	2	2	2	0	4	3	3
Total	Hours	37	16	22	33	41	49	38
	Full-time Staff	4	2	2	4	4	4	4
	Part-time Staff	3	2	4	1	4	5	5

EXAMINER'S HINT:

Tables like this one can be complicated, so do make sure you know how they work before you answer any questions.

With so many possible sets of data you are spoilt for choice. However guesswork won't do. The data (about the number of part-time staff) required to answer this question is on the bottom row.

RANGE = Largest value - Smallest value

$$= 5 - 1 = 4 \text{ Part-time staff}$$

$$\text{AVERAGE} = \frac{\text{Total of all the Values}}{\text{Number of Values}}$$

$$= \frac{3+2+4+1+4+5+5}{7}$$

$$= \frac{24}{7} = 3.43 \text{ Part-time staff}$$

TASK 3

Use the table above to find...

1. ... the range of the number of hours worked by full-time members of staff on Sunday.
2. ... the average number of hours worked by full-time members of staff on Sunday.
3. ... the range of the number of hours worked by Hassan each week.
4. ... the average number of hours worked by Hassan each week.
5. ... the range of the number of hours worked by all members of staff on Saturday.
6. ... the average number of hours worked by all members of staff on Saturday.

LEVEL OF ACCURACY

You need to know how to work to the level of accuracy you have been told to use.

Rounding Whole Numbers

EXAMINER'S HINT:

In the test you will be told the level of accuracy you must work to. However, when you are producing work for your portfolio you will need to use your common sense. The level of accuracy you work to will largely depend on the purpose of your work.

Level of accuracy means rounding a number to the nearest **1000**, **100**, **1**, $\frac{1}{10}$, $\frac{1}{100}$ etc. Look at the place value table below.

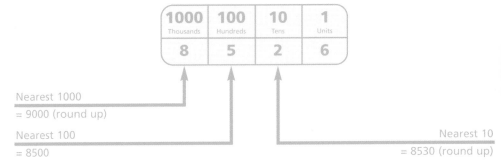

The digit to the right of the one you are working to will tell you if you need to round up. For example, when rounding a number to the **nearest ten** you need to look at the digit in the units column. If it is **5 or more**, the digit in the tens column is **rounded up**. If it is **4 or less** the digit in the tens column **stays the same**. The digit in the units column then becomes a zero, showing the number to the nearest 10.

EXAMINER'S HINT:

In our example, 8526 rounded to the nearest 10 is 8530. However, you should realise that any number between 8525 and 8534 rounded to the nearest 10 is 8530.

TASK 1

① Correct the number **4716** to the nearest ten, hundred and thousand.
② The number of pupils who attend school on a particular day is **800** to the nearest **100**. What is the smallest and largest possible number of pupils who attended school on that day?

Rounding Decimals

EXAMINER'S HINT:

Unless the question tells you otherwise, always give money to 2 decimal places. Amounts of money are rounded in exactly the same way as decimals and whole numbers.

Decimals are rounded in exactly the same way as whole numbers. To give a number to **1 decimal place**, you round to the nearest tenth ($\frac{1}{10}$) so that there is only one digit after the decimal point. To give a number to **2 decimal places**, you round to the nearest hundredth ($\frac{1}{100}$) so that there are two digits after the decimal point.

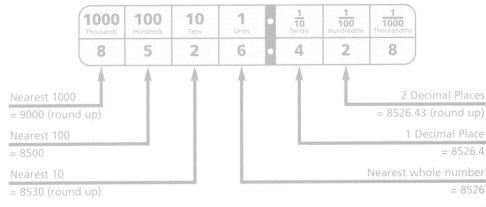

TASK 2

Correct the number **45 803.563** to:

① the nearest ten   ③ the nearest whole number   ⑤ the nearest hundred
② 1 decimal place   ④ the nearest ten thousand   ⑥ 2 decimal places

You must be able to identify suitable calculations to get the results you need for your task and check your calculations using different methods to ensure they make sense. You must also be able to describe how the results of your calculations meet your purpose.

Identifying Calculations

For this course, one of the most important skills is being able to identify the calculation(s) needed to solve a problem or answer a question.

EXAMPLE
Mark saves £4 of his paper round money every week. He wants to buy a computer games consul which costs £120 and has already saved £40. How can he calculate how many more weeks it will take before he can buy the consul?

Mark needs £120	$\longrightarrow$	120
He already has £40	$\longrightarrow$	120 - 40
How many weekly installments of £4 will it take to save this amount?	$\longrightarrow$	$(120 - 40) \div 4$

To work out how many weeks it will be before he can afford the consul, Mark can use the calculation **(120 - 40) ÷ 4** to give him the answer **20 weeks**.

TASK 1
A minicab company charges a booking fee of £2 a journey and £1.50 for every mile travelled. How would you calculate the total charge for a 7 mile journey?

Checking Calculations

It is essential that you check all your calculations for accuracy and sense. You can check your answers make **sense** by using an **estimate**.

EXAMPLE
Simone is buying food for a party. A pack of sausage rolls costs £0.79. Estimate the cost of three packs of sausage rolls. To calculate an estimate, always round the numbers so that you are working with 'easy' numbers.

£0.79 is £1.00 (to the nearest pound) $\longrightarrow$ £1.00 x 3 = £3.00

From this estimate you know that the actual cost of 3 packs will be no more than £3. Therefore, if you have calculated an answer of £23.70 you will easily spot your mistake. The answer is much more likely to be £2.37.

You can check your answers are **accurate** by **working backwards** through the calculation.

$3 \times £0.79 = £2.37 \longrightarrow \dfrac{£2.37}{3} = £0.79$ ✓

TASK 2
Ricky needs to buy 8.85m of thick rope. The rope costs £4 a metre. He calculates that the total cost will be £34.32.

1 ... Make an estimate to check his answer makes sense.

2 ... Work backwards through the calculation to check it for accuracy.

EXAMINER'S HINT:

In your portfolio, always show how you checked your calculations. The assessor will be looking for evidence of this. If you perform lots of similar calculations, you only need to show your checking methods for the first few.

EXAMINER'S HINT:

Working backwards through a calculation is easy. Start with your answer and reverse the maths: addition becomes subtraction, multiplication becomes division and visa versa.

EXAMINER'S HINT:

In your portfolio, you must explain what the results of your calculations mean. Always refer back to your original aims and explain how they have helped you to complete the task. Many candidates perform the calculations and just write down the answer. This is not enough. The numbers are all meaningless if you do not explain them.

You must show that you have developed skills in
- **Interpreting information**
- **Carrying out calculations**
- **Interpreting results and presenting your findings**

The symbols P and T indicate which skills are likely to be required for the portfolio and/or the test.

- Ⓟ ... Portfolio
- Ⓣ ... Test

Interpreting Information

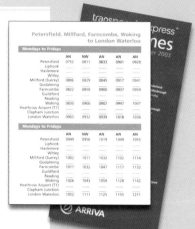

In interpreting information you need to know how to...
- Ⓟ Ⓣ ... obtain relevant information from different sources
- Ⓟ Ⓣ ... read and understand graphs, tables, charts and diagrams
- Ⓟ Ⓣ ... read and understand numbers used in different ways, including negative numbers
- Ⓟ Ⓣ ... estimate amounts and proportions
- Ⓟ Ⓣ ... read scales on a range of equipment to given levels of accuracy
- Ⓟ Ⓣ ... make accurate observations
- Ⓟ Ⓣ ... select appropriate methods for obtaining the results you need, including grouping data when this is appropriate

Carrying Out Calculations

In carrying out calculations you need to know how to...
- Ⓟ Ⓣ ... *show clearly your methods of carrying out calculations and give the level of accuracy of your results
- Ⓟ Ⓣ ... *carry out calculations involving two or more steps, with numbers of any size
- Ⓟ Ⓣ ... convert between fractions, decimals and percentages
- Ⓟ Ⓣ ... convert measurements between systems
- Ⓟ Ⓣ ... work out areas and volumes
- Ⓟ Ⓣ ... work out dimensions from scale drawings
- Ⓟ Ⓣ ... use proportion and calculate using ratios where appropriate
- Ⓟ Ⓣ ... compare sets of data with a minimum of 20 items
- Ⓟ Ⓣ ... use range to describe the spread within sets of data
- Ⓟ Ⓣ ... understand and use given formulae
- Ⓟ Ⓣ ... check your methods in ways that pick up faults and make sure your results make sense

Albert Einstein (1879-1955)

Interpreting Results and Presenting Your Findings

In interpreting results and presenting your findings you need to know how to...
- Ⓟ Ⓣ ... select effective ways to present your findings
- Ⓟ Ⓣ ... construct and use graphs, charts and diagrams, and follow accepted conventions for labelling these
- Ⓟ Ⓣ ... highlight the main points of your findings and describe your methods
- Ⓟ ... explain how the results of calculations meet the purpose of your activity

EXAMINER'S HINT:

A number scale can be a very useful aid for you to understand positive and negative numbers.

BIGGER

POSITIVE

NEGATIVE

SMALLER

> You should be able to read and understand numbers used in different ways, including negative numbers.

When you use positive and negative numbers, zero is the fixed point on the scale. All numbers relate to this point. Above zero, the numbers are positive (+). Below zero, the numbers are negative (-). Positive and negative numbers are often used in everyday life e.g. to show temperatures above and below freezing or financial profit and loss.

EXAMPLE

The temperature at midday is 5°C. By 8pm it has fallen by 8 degrees. What is the temperature at 8pm?

The temperature has **fallen**, so you need to **subtract**. To **subtract** you count **down** the number scale, so the answer will be **smaller**.

At 8pm the temperature is -3°C.

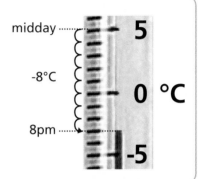

midday ······· 5

-8°C

0 °C

8pm ·······➤

-5

You can use a calculator to produce work for your portfolio. This means you can work with larger numbers.

EXAMPLE

LONSDALE BUILDING SOCIETY

Date	Description	Deposit	Withdrawal	Balance
11/12/03				£226.30
12/12/03	The Toy Shop		-£49.99	£176.31
13/12/03	Gas Bill		-£21.03	£155.28
14/12/03	Cheque	£25.00		£180.28
16/12/03	La Trattoria		-£32.98	£147.30
19/12/03	Rent		-£260.00	-£112.70

Look at the bank statement above. What would the new balance be on 19/12/03 if £50.00 cash was paid into the account on that day?

To **add** you count **up** the number scale, so the answer will be **bigger**.

Using a calculator, the correct answer is, **–£62.70**.

EXAMINER'S HINT:

-£62.70 is a bigger number than -£112.70 because it is closer to zero. In terms of money, it means less money is owed to the bank so the debt is smaller.

TASK 1

1 ... Arrange the following numbers in order of size, with the smallest first:
3, -32, 46, -65, 1, 7, -20, 13, -1, 0.

2 ... Which of the following number ranges is the largest?
-10 to 10, -5 to 5, -25 to 0, 5 to 20, -25 to -5.

3 ... At 6pm the temperature in Oslo was -6°C and the temperature in Cairo was 21°C. What is the difference in temperature between Oslo and Cairo?

4 ... A bank statement has a balance of £23.40. What would the balance become if £78 was withdrawn from the account?

You need to be able to convert between fractions, decimals and percentages.

For each of the flow charts below there are three starting points - **Fractions**, **Decimals** and **Percentages**. Trace around the charts and see how you can move from one system to another by following simple rules.

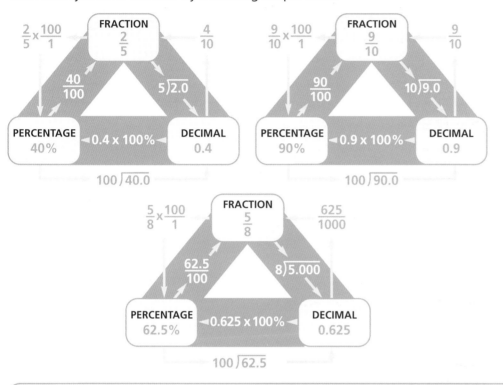

$\frac{2}{5} \times \frac{100}{1}$ FRACTION $\frac{2}{5}$ $\frac{4}{10}$

$\frac{40}{100}$ $5\overline{)2.0}$

PERCENTAGE 40% ◄ 0.4 x 100% ◄ DECIMAL 0.4

$100\overline{)40.0}$

$\frac{9}{10} \times \frac{100}{1}$ FRACTION $\frac{9}{10}$ $\frac{9}{10}$

$\frac{90}{100}$ $10\overline{)9.0}$

PERCENTAGE 90% ◄ 0.9 x 100% ◄ DECIMAL 0.9

$100\overline{)90.0}$

$\frac{5}{8} \times \frac{100}{1}$ FRACTION $\frac{5}{8}$ $\frac{625}{1000}$

$\frac{62.5}{100}$ $8\overline{)5.000}$

PERCENTAGE 62.5% ◄ 0.625 x 100% ◄ DECIMAL 0.625

$100\overline{)62.5}$

EXAMINER'S HINT:

Use rough paper for your calculations and refer back to Level 1 (page 12) if help is needed.

EXAMPLE

A snooker club has 250 registered members. Only 50 members visit the club more than two times a week.

a) What fraction of the registered members visit the club more than twice a week?

b) What is this fraction as a percentage?

EXAMINER'S HINT:

Refer back to the section about Simple Fractions at Level 1 (page 8). When a pizza is divided into four equal slices, the 'value' of one slice is $\frac{1}{4}$. Exactly the same principle applies here.

a) 50 out of the 250 members visit the club more than two times a week. This can be written as $\frac{50}{250}$. Give the answer in its simplest form.

$$\frac{50}{250} = \frac{1}{5} \text{ of the members}$$

b) Having found the fraction, it is easy to find the percentage using the rule shown above.

$$\frac{1}{5} \times \frac{100}{1} = \frac{100}{5} = 20\%$$

EXAMINER'S HINT:

Remember, you can always build a fraction chain to help you with your calculations (see page 8).

TASK 2

① ... An advertising slogan states '8 out of 10 people prefer it!' What percentage of people, are they claiming, prefer their product?

② ... A violin weighs 0.5 kg. Its travel case weighs 3kg. What is the weight of the travel case as a fraction of the total weight? What is this as a percentage? Give your answer to 2 decimal places.

> You must be able to estimate amounts and proportions and read scales on a range of equipment to given levels of accuracy.

Estimating Amounts and Proportions

At Level 1, you learned how to calculate an estimate by rounding numbers (see page 29). At this level, you also need to be able to estimate amounts and proportions based upon information you are given and your own observations.

There are two key points to remember when making an estimate:
- Always round numbers so that you are working with 'easy' numbers
- Trust your own judgement

EXAMINER'S HINT:

You can practise making estimates at home. Estimate the height, width and weight of everyday objects e.g. chairs, tables, the television. Compare them to things you know the length/weight of. Remember, a ruler is roughly 30cm long and a bag of sugar weighs 1kg.

EXAMPLE

David is concerned that the tree in his back garden is getting too close to the overhead telegraph wires. The picture opposite shows the height of the tree in relation to the height of the overhead wires.

The overhead wires are 18 metres high. Estimate the height of the tree.

A 7m   **B** 10m   **C** 12m   **D** 15m

Estimates like this are simple comparisons. The correct answer is 10m (**B**).

The telegraph wires are 20m (rounded to the nearest 10) and the tree is roughly half the height of the wires.

TASK 1

1. ... The diagrams below show two plans for a garden. Estimate the area of the decking as a fraction of the garden's total area for each plan.

2. ... Estimate the volume of liquid in this pint glass.

3. ... An apple weighs 153g. Estimate the total weight of the fruit.

Reading Scales

Reading scales to a given level of accuracy is similar to rounding numbers.

EXAMPLE

What is the reading on the dial in kilograms and grams, to the nearest 50g?

First, you need to identify the count pattern of the scale (see page 16). This scale climbs in 50 gram intervals with 10 gram divisions in between.

The indicator is between 1kg 350g and 1kg 400g. It is **more than halfway** between the measurements so, **round up**.

The reading is 1kg 400g to the nearest 50g.

EXAMINER'S HINT:

If the indicator is **less than halfway** between the two measurements, **round down**.

In some cases, the pointer will fall between the marked divisions on a scale. Rather than round up or down, you can estimate a reading.

EXAMPLE

Estimate the time on this watch, to the nearest minute.

The count pattern on this watch climbs in 1 hour/5 minute intervals. The minute hand is between the divisions for 1 and 2, so it is between 5 and 10 minutes past the hour. It is just over halfway between the two (which would be 7.5min), so we can estimate it is 8 minutes past five to the nearest minute.

EXAMINER'S HINT:

Imagine extra divisions on a scale and their equivalent values to help you make an estimate.

TASK 2

For each of the scales below, estimate a reading. Then round the reading to an appropriate level of accuracy.

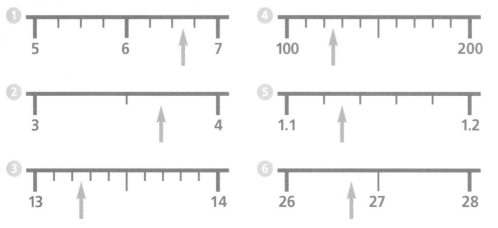

CONVERTING MEASUREMENTS

> You should be able to convert measurements between systems.

Life is never simple and you will find that we use different units for measuring the same thing. For example, hospitals use metric units (kilograms) when weighing babies, but most parents want to know the weight of their baby in pounds and ounces. You will already be familiar with converting measurements within the same system from Level 1 (see page 16). At Level 2, you need to take it one step further and convert measurements between systems.

EXAMPLE

A travel agent exchanges currency at a rate of €1.60 (euros) for every £1 (pound sterling). Calculate how many euros Jack will get if he exchanges £100. No commission is charged.

The exchange rate is £1 = €1.60
Therefore £100 = 100 x €1.60 = €160

TASK 1

Use the exchange rate above to convert...
1. ... £10 into euros
2. ... £40 into euros
3. ... €320 into pounds
4. ... €96 into pounds

EXAMINER'S HINT:

In the test you will not be allowed to use a calculator so make sure that you can multiply decimals (see page 11).

EXAMPLE

A tank holds 6 gallons of petrol. One gallon is equal to 4.55 litres. Calculate the number of litres the tank holds to the nearest litre.

We know that 1 gallon = 4.55 litres
Therefore, 6 gallons = 6 x 4.55 litres = 27.30 litres
So, the tank holds 27 litres (to the nearest litre)

TASK 2

1. ... A woman weighs 9 stones. One stone is equal to 6.3 kilograms. What is her weight to the nearest kilogram?
2. ... A cyclist travels a distance of 9 000 metres. How far does he cycle, to the nearest mile, if 1 mile is equal to 1 600m?

EXAMPLE

A keep fit enthusiast runs a distance of 12 000m. If 1 mile is equal to 1.6 kilometres how far does he run to the nearest mile?

Before you tackle a question like this, think about what you need to do and how you will arrive at your answer. Break the process down into simple stages. To answer this question, you need to convert 12 000m into kilometres and then convert the distance in kilometres into miles. Finally, you then have to correct the answer to the nearest mile.

EXAMINER'S HINT:

At Level 2, you should be able to carry out calculations involving two or more steps with numbers of any size, as illustrated by the example on the left. However you should realise that calculations involving two or more steps apply to the whole of Level 2 and not just this section.

Step One: Convert distance from metres to kilometres

We know that ⟶ 1 000m = 1km

Therefore, 12 000m ⟶ $= \frac{12\,000}{1\,000}$ km = 12km

Step Two: Convert distance from kilometres to miles

We know that ⟶ 1.6km = 1 mile

Therefore, 12km ⟶ $= \frac{12}{1.6}$ miles = 7.5 miles

Step Three: Correct answer to the nearest mile

7.5 miles ⟶ to the nearest mile = 8 miles

EXAMINER'S HINT:

If 1 mile is equal to 1.6km then 1.6km is equal to 1 mile. Don't be afraid to reverse the conversion if it makes it easier.

TASK 3

1. ... A cyclist travels a distance of 11 miles. If 1 mile is equal to 1.6km what distance does he cycle to the nearest hundred metres.

2. ... A fully grown male Asian elephant weighs 124 hundredweight. How much does the elephant weigh in kilograms if 20 hundredweight is equal to 1 ton and 1 ton is equal to 1 020kg?

3. ... An estate agent sells a property with 3 acres of land. What is the area of this land to the nearest square metre if 1 acre is equal to 4 840yd² and 1m² is equal to 1.09yd²?

EXAMINER'S HINT:

Think about the information you have been given in the question and what you already know (e.g. how many metres are in a kilometre). You need to combine this information to answer the question correctly.

Always refer back to the question to ensure you give the answer to the required level of accuracy.

> You should be able to use proportion and calculate using ratios where appropriate.

At Level 1, you learned that, when calculating using ratios and proportion, it is crucial to know...
> ... what the whole is.
> ... how many parts the whole is divided into.
> ... how to turn the question around to find the answer you need.

At Level 2, you will need to perform calculations that have two or more steps. However, the processes involved will be exactly the same.

EXAMINER'S HINT:

Always read the question carefully to avoid silly mistakes.

EXAMPLE

This label shows the nutritional information for semi-skimmed milk. What is the ratio of fat to carbohydrate?

NUTRITIONAL INFORMATION	
Typical values	Per 100ml
Energy	210kJ
	50kcal
Protein	3g
Carbohydrate	4.8g
Fat	1.8g
Fibre	nil
Sodium	0.1g
Calcium	120mg

Step One: Identify the ratio.
There is 1.8g of fat and 4.8g of carbohydrate.

Ratio of fat to carbohydrate
   $= 1.8 : 4.8$

Step two: Simplify the ratio.
Multiply both sides of the ratio by the same number (try 10 or 100) so that you are working with whole numbers.

$$1.8 : 4.8$$
$$= 1.8 \times 10 : 4.8 \times 10$$
$$= 18 : 48$$

Step three: Simplify the numbers to give the final answer.

$$18 : 48$$
$$= \frac{18}{2} : \frac{48}{2}$$
$$= 9 : 24$$
$$= \frac{9}{3} : \frac{24}{3}$$
$$= 3 : 8$$

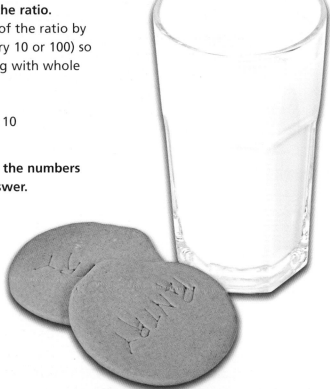

TASK 1

1 ... Using the label above what is the ratio of protein to fat?
2 ... A food label states that a single serving contains 3.2g of protein, 17.6g of carbohydrate and 24g of fat. What is the ratio of protein to carbohydrate to fat?

EXAMPLE

A company gives its marketing department £12 000. The money is to be divided between exhibitions, advertising and catalogue production in the ratio 5:3:1. How much money is allocated to each item to the nearest pound?

| EXHIBITIONS | ADVERTISING | CATALOGUE |

Step One: Identify the whole.
Whole = £12 000

Step Two: Find the number of parts the whole is divided into.
When working with ratios, you simply add all the digits in the ratio together to find the total number of parts.
5 + 3 + 1 = 9 parts

Step Three: Find the value of one part
1 part = $\frac{12\ 000}{9}$ = £1333.33

Step Four: Calculate how much money is allocated to each item.
Exhibitions (5 parts) = 5 x £1333.33 = £6666.65
                       = £6667 (to the nearest pound)
Advertising (3 parts) = 3 x £1333.33 = £3999.99
                       = £4000 (to the nearest pound)
Catalogue (1 part)   = 1 x £1333.33 = £1333.33
                       = £1333 (to the nearest pound)

EXAMINER'S HINT:

In the test, the calculations will usually give simple answers. When working with 'real' figures for your portfolio the numbers will not be so straightforward, but you can use a calculator to help you.

EXAMINER'S HINT:

When you are calculating with money, it makes sense to work to two decimal places, showing pounds and pence, unless you are instructed otherwise.

EXAMINER'S HINT:

Read these questions carefully - they are multi-stage calculations.

TASK 2

1. ... £10 is divided between three children in the ratio of their ages. Jack is 11 years old, Mary is 8 years old and Jenny is 6 years old. Work out how much each child will receive without using a calculator?

2. ... A builder makes concrete by mixing cement, gravel, sand and water in the ratio 2:8:5:3 by weight. Use your calculator to work out how many kilograms of sand he needs to make 10 000kg of concrete.

3. ... The angles in a quadrilateral are in the ratio 3:4:5:6. If all the angles add up to 360°, what is the difference between the largest and the smallest angle?

4. ... A car park has 55 parking spaces. Five spaces are reserved for visitors and 12% of the remaining spaces are reserved for disabled drivers. Work out how many spaces are available for general use without using a calculator.

5. ... A gardener prepares some trays of plants to sell. A tray normally contains 20 plants. He plants 20% extra in each tray in case some of the plants fail to grow. How many plants will there be in a tray if only two fail to grow? Work out the answer without using a calculator.

> **You must be able to understand and use given formulae.**

Formulae show the relationship between two or more changeable quantities. They can be written in words, but most often symbols are used instead. Here are two examples of common formulae written in words and then written using symbols.

The area of a rectangular shape is equal to its length multiplied by its width.

$$A = lw$$

The speed of a moving object is equal to the distance it travels divided by the time it takes to travel that distance.

$$S = \frac{d}{t}$$

There are two formulae which are commonly used to find the area of a circle, where **r** is the radius of the circle:

$$\text{AREA} = 3r^2$$

$$\text{AREA} = \pi r^2$$

Pi (π) is the ratio of a circle's circumference to its diameter. It has a value of 3.14159265. If it appears in a test question you will be given a value to use for pi, usually to two decimal places e.g. 3.14. Pi should be treated in exactly the same way as any other symbol in a formula.

EXAMPLE

Calculate the area of the mosaic table top shown. The area of a circle is given by the formula: $A = \pi r^2$, where $\pi = 3$.

Using the formula...

$$A = \pi r^2$$
$$= 3 \times 0.6^2$$
$$= 3 \times (0.6 \times 0.6)$$
$$= 3 \times 0.36$$

Area = 1.08m²

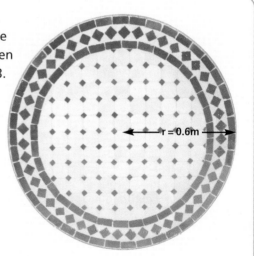

r = 0.6m

TASK 1

Answer the following questions without using a calculator.

1 ... Calculate the area of a circle of radius 6cm if **a)** $\pi = 3$ and **b)** if $\pi = 3.14$.

2 ... The circumference of a circle is given by the formula $C = \pi d$ where **d** is diameter. Calculate the circumference of a circle of diameter 4.8cm if $\pi = 3$.

3 ... The voltage (V) needed to send a current (I) through an electrical device is given by the formula $V = IR$, where **R** is resistance of the electrical device. Calculate the voltage needed to send a current of 0.45 amps through the device if it has a resistance of 13 ohms. Voltage is measured in volts.

Some of the formulae you see in the test may be unfamiliar. Regardless of what the formula looks like, all you are doing is substituting numbers for symbols (or vice versa).

TASK 2

1 ... The formula that converts a temperature reading from degrees Celsius (°C) into degrees Fahrenheit (°F) is...

$$F = \frac{9}{5}C + 32$$

What is the temperature in degrees Fahrenheit, to the nearest degree, if the temperature in degrees Celsius is 22°C?

2 ... The volume of a cone is given by the formula...

$$\text{Volume} = \frac{1}{3}\pi r^2 h$$

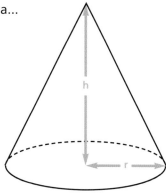

Calculate the volume of a cone if
r = 4cm, h = 6.8cm, π = 3.

3 ... The distance travelled (s) by an object depends on its initial speed (u), final speed (v) and time of travel (t), and is given by the formula...

$$s = \left(\frac{u + v}{2}\right)t$$

Calculate the distance travelled in metres if
initial speed = 4m/s, final speed = 12m/s, time = 5.5s.

4 ... A local council offers residents a 'Leisure Card' where the card entitles the holder to 20% discount on the entrance prices to council-run leisure facilities and fitness classes.

Which formula shows the total cost for one year, for a leisure card holder who attends two swimming sessions and one yoga class a week where C = the total cost, s = the normal cost for a swimming session and y = the normal cost for a yoga class?

A $C = 52(2s + y)$

B $C = 52\left((2s + y) \times \frac{20}{100}\right)$

C $C = 52\left((2s + y) \times \frac{80}{100}\right)$

D $C = 2s + y - 20$

5 ... A mail order company buys stock at wholesale prices. They calculate the sale price, at which it is sold to customers, by increasing the wholesale price by 60% and adding a charge of £2.50 per item to cover packaging and delivery. Devise your own formula for calculating the sale price of stock.

You should be able to work out areas and volumes.

Calculating Areas

EXAMPLE

A property developer decides to sand and varnish the floorboards in the living room of one of his houses. One tin of varnish will cover 6m². If he wants to apply two coats of varnish to the whole floor, how many tins of varnish will he need to buy?

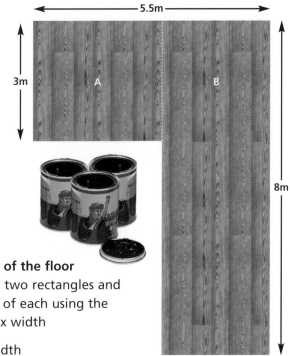

Step One: Work out the area of the floor

Divide the floor up into two rectangles and then work out the area of each using the formula: Area = length x width

Area of A = length x width
= 3 x (5.5 – 2.5)
= 3 x 3 = 9m²

Area of B = length x width
= 8 x 2.5 = 20m²

Total Area = Area of A + Area of B = 9 + 20 = **29m²**

Step Two: Calculate how many tins of varnish are required

If one tin of varnish covers 6m²...

Then $\frac{29}{6}$ = 4.83 tins are required for one coat of varnish

Therefore 4.83 x 2 = 9.66 tins are required for two coats of varnish.

The developer needs to buy **10 tins** of varnish to apply two coats to the floor.

TASK 1

Calculate the areas of the following shapes. They are not drawn to scale.

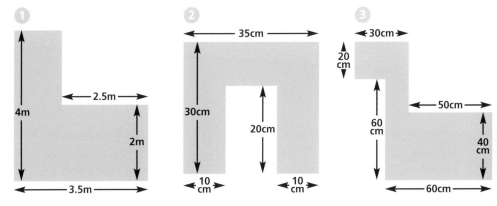

Calculating Volumes

EXAMPLE

Internally a large chest freezer is 6 feet by 3 feet by 3.5 feet in dimension. It contains six wire baskets for holding frozen food, which fill the freezer completely. If all the baskets are exactly the same size, what is the volume of one basket in cubic metres? 1 cubic foot = $0.027m^3$. Give your answer to two decimal places.

Step One: Calculate the volume of the freezer.
Volume = length x width x height
Volume = 6 x 3 x 3.5 = 63 cubic feet

Step Two: Find the volume of one basket
Volume of one Basket = $\frac{63}{6}$ = 10.5 cubic feet

Step 3: Convert from cubic feet to cubic metres
We know that 1 cubic foot = $0.027m^3$
Therefore 10.5 cubic feet = 10.5 x 0.027
  = $0.28m^3$ (to 2 decimal places)

EXAMINER'S HINT:

Always take a moment to think about the question and what you actually need to do before you begin.

TASK 2

① A factory worker packs tins into cardboard boxes. If the tins have to be placed upright, how many will fit in each box?

② These questions refer to the same box and tin as in question 1.
a) Calculate the volume of each tin. Use π = 3.
b) Calculate the total volume of all the tins that will fit in the box.
c) What percentage of the space inside the box do the tins take up?

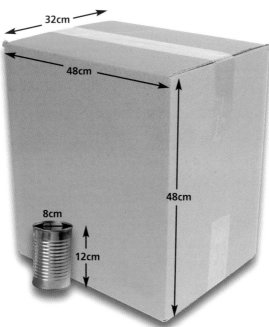

EXAMINER'S HINT:

You need to know that the formula for calculating diameter is **d = 2r**, where **d** is the diameter and **r** is the radius of a circle.

In Question 1, if you work out the volume of 1 tin and then divide into the volume of the box you will get an **incorrect** answer - so think about it carefully.

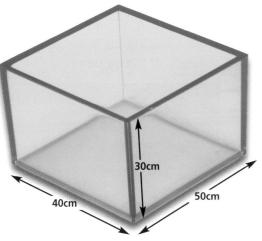

③ Water is allowed to flow into the tank shown at a rate of 0.48 litres per second. To begin with the tank is empty. Will the tank be overflowing after 2 minutes? Explain your answer.

EXAMINER'S HINT:

You need to know how to convert cm^3 into litres (see page 15).

You need to be able to work out dimensions from scale drawings.

If a drawing is 'to scale', it means that the sizes of the 'objects' in the drawing are directly proportional to the actual sizes of the 'objects' in real life. Scales are written in the same ways as ratios e.g. 1:20. A scale of 1:20 means that one unit of measurement in the drawing represents 20 units of measurement in real life.

EXAMINER'S HINT:

Remember, not all diagrams on the test paper will be drawn to scale. The ones that are will be clearly labelled.

EXAMPLE

The diagram shows a scale drawing of a coffee table top. The scale of the drawing is 1:20. Calculate the actual surface area of the top of the coffee table.

From the information given we know that every 1cm on the drawing represents 20cm. Also, since the question is an area calculation, we need to know the actual length and width of the table top.

Step One: Measure the length and width on the scale drawing using a ruler.
Length = 7cm and Width = 4.5cm.

Step Two: Convert these scale measurements into actual measurements.
Scale length = 7cm and so actual length = 7cm x 20 = 140cm.
Scale width = 4.5cm and so actual width = 4.5cm x 20 = 90cm.

EXAMINER'S HINT:

Areas of rectangles were dealt with on page 18. Check back if you are unsure.

Step Three: Calculate the actual area of the coffee table.
Area = length x width
Area = 140cm x 90cm = 12 600cm^2.

TASK 1

① The diagram shows a scale drawing of an empty picture frame. The scale of the drawing is 1:10. Calculate the actual area of the frame.

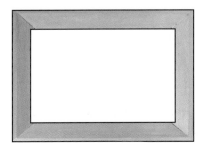

② The diagram shows a scale drawing of a garden where 1cm represents 5m. Calculate the actual perimeter length of the garden.

EXAMPLE

A motorist needs to travel from Plymouth to Newquay. The scale on his map is 1cm:10km. Use the map to calculate approximately how far the journey is by road, to the nearest kilometre.

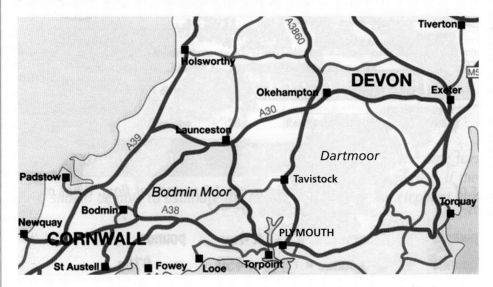

The distance from Plymouth to Newquay on the map is approximately 7cm.

... From the information given we know that 1cm on the map represents 10km.

... Therefore 7cm = 7 x 10km = 70km.

... The approximate distance from Plymouth to Newquay is **70km**.

TASK 2

Use the map above to answer the following questions...

1 ... A motorist is travelling from Exeter to Plymouth via Okehampton. Calculate this distance to the nearest kilometre.

2 ... A motorist reckons that to travel from Exeter to Plymouth and call in at Torquay on the way is a journey of approximately 130km. Is he correct? Give reasons for your answer.

3 ... A motorist is travelling from Holsworthy to Newquay. Calculate this distance to the nearest mile, if 1 mile is equal to 1 600m.

TASK 3

This diagram (not to scale) shows the positions within a town of the school (S), church (C), newsagent (N) and butcher (B).

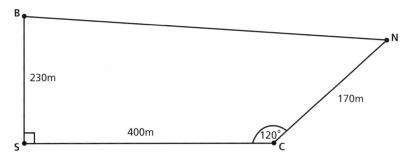

a) Draw a scale drawing to show the positions of the school, church, newsagent and butcher.

b) James walks from the school to the newsagent in a direct line. How far does he walk in km?

EXAMINER'S HINT:

If you need to produce a scale drawing, you simply reverse the process shown above. Start with the actual measurements, decide on an appropriate scale and then scale down the actual measurements.

You need to be able to obtain relevant information from different sources, make accurate observations and select appropriate methods for obtaining the results you need, including grouping data when this is appropriate.

EXAMINER'S HINT:

A typical example of source material used in the test is a timetable. Look at train and bus timetables for local services to make sure you are confident reading them.

EXAMPLE

A rail company operating trains out of Petersfield decides to offer cheap 'Off Peak' fares on services that arrive at London Waterloo after 10am. If a customer who usually catches the 0833 service from Petersfield decides to wait for the first Off Peak train, to take advantage of the offer, what will be the difference in his journey time?

Petersfield, Millford, Farncombe, Woking to London Waterloo

Mondays to Fridays

	AN	NW	AN	AN	AN
Petersfield	0752	0811	0833	0901	0928
Liphook	—	—	—	—	—
Haslemere	—	—	—	—	—
Witley	—	—	—	—	—
Millford (Surrey)	0806	0829	0845	0917	0941
Godalming	—	—	—	—	—
Farncombe	0822	0850	0900	0937	0959
Guildford	—	—	—	—	—
Reading	—	—	—	—	—
Woking	0830	0900	0907	0947	1007
Heathrow Airport (T1)	—	—	—	—	—
Clapham Junction	—	—	—	—	—
London Waterloo	0903	0932	0939	1018	1036

Mondays to Fridays

	AN	NW	AN	AN	AN
Petersfield	0949	0956	1019	1049	1055
Liphook	—	—	—	—	—
Haslemere	—	—	—	—	—
Witley	—	—	—	—	—
Millford (Surrey)	1002	1011	1032	1102	1114
Godalming	—	—	—	—	—
Farncombe	1017	1032	1047	1117	1132
Guildford	—	—	—	—	—
Reading	—	—	—	—	—
Woking	1026	1043	1059	1128	1142
Heathrow Airport (T1)	—	—	—	—	—
Clapham Junction	—	—	—	—	—
London Waterloo	1052	1111	1125	1155	1211

The first thing to do is to identify the relevant data. This is in the third and fourth columns of the timetable shown above and has been highlighted for this purpose.

- **Usual journey time** → = Arrival Time - Departure Time
  = 0939hrs – 0833hrs
  = 1hr 6min

- **Off Peak journey time** → = Arrival Time – Departure Time
  = 1018hrs – 0901hrs
  = 1hr 17min

- **Difference in journey time** → = 1hr 17min – 1hr 6min
  = 11min

TASK 1

Use the timetable above to answer the following questions...

1. ... Grace wants to arrive in London before midday. What is the latest train she can catch from Millford station to get there in time? How long will her train journey take?
2. ... Simon needs to get to Woking by 11.15am because he has a job interview. What is the time of the last train he can catch from Farncombe?
3. ... What is the difference between the average journey time of Peak Time trains and the average journey time of Off Peak trains travelling from Petersfield to London Waterloo?
4. ... What percentage of trains departing from Woking Station take less than 30 minutes to arrive at London Waterloo?

Finding Information for Your Portfolio

The first step in obtaining relevant information is to identify suitable sources. There is a huge range of sources readily available to you, including newspapers, the Internet, magazines and journals, books, catalogues, brochures, reports, leaflets and other publications. The information could take the form of text, numbers or graphs and charts. You might even collect your own data firsthand, by recording measurements or observations.

The sources you use for portfolio work will depend on the purpose of your activity. For example, if you are comparing the efficiency of local transport services, the following sources are available:

- Timetables published by the different travel companies e.g. buses, trains, trams.
- Fare prices for different types of transport.
- Firsthand data (collected yourself) of the number of passengers using different services.
- Details of any special travel offers.
- Service records published by the local rail network.
- Questionnaires completed by users of the different services.
- National statistics about travel and transport from the Internet.

TASK 2

Holidays in Nice, Saltzburg and Vienna

Location	Activity	Nights	Cost	Departure Date	Departure Day	Departure Airport
Nice						
	Sailing	7	£299.00	06/01/2004	Tue	Southampton
	Scuba Diving	7	£385.00	12/06/2004	Sat	Birmingham
	Windsurfing	7	£250.00	01/07/2004	Thu	Edinburgh
Saltzburg						
	Abseiling	10	£655.00	23/06/2004	Wed	Cardiff
	Climbing	7	£45.00	13/08/2001	Sat	Southingham
	Climbing	7	£399.00	21/12/2004	Sun	Birmingham
Vienice						
	Scuba Diving	14	£690.00	01/06/2004	Cardiff	Tue
Vienna						
	Mountain Biking	7	£345.00	01/07/2004	Thu	Birmingham
	River Rafting	10	£760.00	17/03/2004	Wed	Birmingham

1 ... This table containing holiday information was found on the Internet. Look at it carefully. Would you be happy to include this table in your own portfolio as source material? Explain your answer.

2 ... A student decides to see if there is a relationship between the number of holiday makers travelling to different European destinations and the prices of package holidays. Make a list of possible sources where she could obtain relevant information for this activity.

EXAMINER'S HINT:

Always include a record of any firsthand data in your portfolio, with a description of where and how you collected it.

EXAMINER'S HINT:

When carrying out a substantial activity for your portfolio you need to use information from two different sources, one of which must include a graph.

If it is difficult to find a graph, you can collect data in a different format and present it as a graph yourself. For example, a comparison of fare prices for different types of transport over the same journey could be shown graphically.

EXAMINER'S HINT:

Whatever sources you use to obtain information, it is important that you check the data for possible mistakes and inaccuracies before you use it in your portfolio.

Data can be collected firsthand by accurately recording measurements or observations. To make sense of the data it is then often **grouped** together in a frequency table. There are two different types of data that you can record.

Recording Discrete Data

Discrete data can only have certain values and each is separate from the next. There are no 'in between' values.

EXAMINER'S HINT:

Frequency simply means the number of times an event occurs. In our example, there were 4 thirty second intervals when one car passed Jane's house, 7 when two cars passed the house etc.

The tally column is not essential but it can reduce the chance of you making a mistake.

Always total up the frequency column to check that all the data has been included in the table.

EXAMPLE

Jane is carrying out a traffic survey. She records the number of cars that pass her house every 30 seconds for a period of 20 minutes. Group her data in a frequency table.

Number of Cars

4	3	4	1	2	5	5	4	3	2
4	5	3	2	4	4	4	5	5	1
2	4	3	5	4	3	3	5	2	4
2	4	3	5	2	1	1	4	5	3

Number of Cars	Tally	Frequency
1	IIII	4
2	HHH II	7
3	HHH III	8
4	HHH HHH II	12
5	HHH IIII	9
		40

TASK 3

1 ... Bolton Wanderers scored the following number of goals in the Premier League for the 2002/2003 season. Their scores are shown in red. Group this data in a frequency table.

OPPONENTS	VEN.	ATTN.	RESULT	OPPONENTS	VEN.	ATTN.	RESULT
Fulham	A	16,338	L 4-1	Everton	A	39,480	D 0-0
Charlton Athletic	H	21,753	L 1-2	Aston Villa	A	31,838	L 2-0
Aston Villa	H	22,500	W 1-0	Fulham	H	25,156	D 0-0
Manchester Utd	A	67,623	W 0-1	Charlton Athletic	A	26,057	D 1-1
Liverpool	H	27,378	L 2-3	Newcastle Utd	A	52,005	L 1-0
Arsenal	A	37,974	L 2-1	Everton	H	25,119	L 1-2
Southampton	H	22,692	D 1-1	Birmingham City	H	24,288	W 4-2
Middlesbrough	A	31,005	L 2-0	West Bromwich Alb	A	26,993	D 1-1
Tottenham Hotspur	A	35,909	L 3-1	Manchester Utd	H	27,409	D 1-1
Sunderland	H	23,036	D 1-1	Liverpool	A	41,462	L 2-0
Birmingham City	A	27,224	L 3-1	Sunderland	A	42,124	W 0-2
West Bromwich Alb	H	23,630	D 1-1	Tottenham Hotspur	H	23,084	W 1-0
Leeds Utd	A	36,627	W 2-4	Manchester City	H	26,949	W 2-0
Chelsea	H	25,476	D 1-1	Chelsea	A	39,852	L 1-0
Manchester City	A	34,860	L 2-0	West Ham Utd	H	27,160	W 1-0
Blackburn Rovers	H	24,556	D 1-1	Blackburn Rovers	A	28,862	D 0-0
Leeds Utd	H	23,201	L 0-3	Arsenal	H	27,253	D 2-2
West Ham Utd	A	34,892	D 1-1	Southampton	A	30,951	D 0-0
Newcastle Utd	H	27,314	W 4-3	Middlesbrough	H	22,342	W 2-1

2 ... The test results for a group of students are given below. Group the data to complete the frequency table.

31	61	40	63	65
78	52	57	15	35
77	11	68	46	68
64	70	26	87	49

Test Mark	Tally	Frequency
0 - 19	II	2
20 - 39		
40 - 59		

EXAMINER'S HINT:

In the frequency table for Question 2, the data is grouped into 'Test Mark' ranges: 0-19, 20-39, 40-59 etc. When data is grouped into ranges like this, each range is called a **class interval**.

3 ... Group together the data for the attendance figures at Bolton matches (shown above) in a frequency table using four equal class intervals.

Recording Continuous Data

Continuous data can have any value. It tends to be obtained by using measuring instruments. The accuracy is dependent on the precision of the equipment.

EXAMPLE

John has recorded the temperature at midday everyday for the month of June using a thermometer. All the temperatures are to the nearest degree Celsius. Group together John's results in a frequency table.

Temperature, T (°C)	Tally	Frequency
5<T≤10	III	3
10<T≤15	۱۱۱۱ ۱۱۱۱ IIII	14
15<T≤20	۱۱۱۱ ۱۱۱۱ I	11
20<T≤25	II	2
		30

EXAMINER'S HINT:

A temperature measurement of 16°C to the nearest degree can have any value from 15.5°C to 16.4°C. This is why the measurements are an example of continuous data.

As you can see, the temperature column in this table is arranged in groups of five degrees. These groups are called **class intervals**. A class interval of 5<T≤10 includes any temperature that is greater than 5°C and is less than or equal to 10°C. The other class intervals follow the same pattern.

TASK 4

1 ... Emma decided to measure the height (h) of all the students in her class. Here are the results, to the nearest cm:
171, 178, 166, 173, 180, 173, 186, 176, 170, 184, 178, 174, 169, 189, 175, 182, 181, 171, 179, 164, 178, 175, 174, 191, 169, 178, 173, 188, 167, 192.
Sort the data into a frequency table using class intervals 160<h≤165, 165<h≤170 etc.

2 ... The individual weights of 40 people, to the nearest kg, are as follows:
79, 75, 68, 70, 83, 72, 81, 89, 61, 74, 80, 51, 84, 63, 73, 54, 76, 74, 80, 85, 94, 77, 71, 81, 70, 66, 87, 62, 59, 63, 63, 67, 75, 81, 80, 78, 60, 77, 61, 75.
Sort the data into a frequency table using appropriate class intervals.

> You need to be able to select effective ways to present your findings.
> You should also be able to understand, construct and use graphs, charts
> and diagrams, and follow accepted conventions for labelling them.

EXAMINER'S HINT:

When carrying out a task for
your portfolio, don't start until
you know exactly what you
need to find out and who it is
for. If you are not clear about
these two points you will
never be able to select an
effective way to present
your findings.

EXAMINER'S HINT:

If you use Information
Technology to present your
findings it is essential that you
can check the accuracy of, and
explain, the methods you use.

Successful application of number is the ability to identify and carry out the
appropriate calculations to complete any number of practical tasks. The
number skills themselves are tools you employ to achieve your purpose. Many
candidates forget this when producing portfolio work. Remember, your
calculations are all meaningless if you do not explain your findings and
present them in a suitable and effective way.

When presenting your findings, use common sense. Think about...
- **Your Purpose** - what exactly are you trying to achieve?
- **Your Audience** - who will be reading your findings and why?

EXAMPLE

- A commuter on a subway escalator
  has just a couple of seconds to read
  a poster.

  Advertisers use a strong image and
  just a few well-chosen words to get
  their message across.

- Waiting on the platform, the
  commuter might have a few minutes
  to spare before the train arrives.

  Timetables and posters present
  information in a clear, concise and
  easy-to-read format.

- When he arrives at his office, the
  commuter has more time to read
  and understand information.

  Office reports and memos contain
  detailed and complex information.
  They use graphs and diagrams to
  illustrate key points where appropriate.

**Different situations require information
to be presented in different ways.**

TASK 1

For each of these situations, suggest how the information could be presented
effectively. Think about the purpose, the audience and the special requirements
of that particular situation.

1 ... Statistics about last year's flu epidemic, designed to encourage patients
   in a doctor's waiting room to get a vaccination.
2 ... A money-off offer for shoppers in a supermarket.
3 ... A report showing rising crime figures for members attending a
   Neighbourhood Watch meeting.

EXAMINER'S HINT:

Try to use lots of different
methods of presentation in
your portfolio. Repetitive
presentations, which use the
same kind of diagrams, can be
very boring and do not show
off your number skills.

Bar Charts

Bar charts are used to display **discrete** data. As the name suggests, rectangular 'bars' are used to illustrate the data.

EXAMPLE

Draw a bar chart to illustrate the data in the frequency table below.

Number of cars	Frequency
1	4
2	7
3	8
4	12
5	9

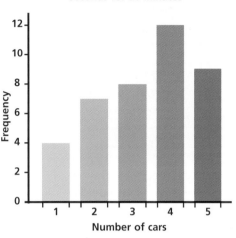

Bar Chart showing the number of cars to pass Jane's house every 30 seconds for 20 minutes

EXAMINER'S HINT:

This bar chart has been generated using 'raw' data that was obtained by carrying out a traffic survey (see page 48). You will notice that it is fairly easy for data to be presented in a visually attractive way without too much effort.

Make sure that your bar chart has labels and a title. Without them the chart is meaningless.

TASK 2

Draw bar charts to illustrate the data in the frequency tables you completed in Task 3 on page 48.

Histograms

A **histogram** is very similar in appearance to a bar chart, but there are no spaces between the bars. Histograms are used to display **continuous** data.

EXAMPLE

Draw a histogram to show the data given in the frequency table below.

Temperature (°C)	Frequency
$5 < T \leqslant 10$	3
$10 < T \leqslant 15$	14
$15 < T \leqslant 20$	11
$20 < T \leqslant 25$	2

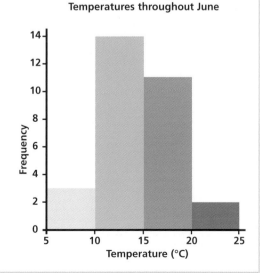

Histogram showing midday Temperatures throughout June

EXAMINER'S HINT:

Make sure that you know the difference between a bar chart and a histogram.

You might have noticed that this histogram was generated using the 'raw' data that was obtained by recording the midday temperature everyday for the month of June (see page 49). Again, data has been presented in a visually attractive way with next to no effort.

As with bar charts, you must make sure that your histogram has labels and a title.

TASK 3

Draw histograms to show the data in the completed frequency tables in Task 4 on page 49.

Pie Charts

Pie charts use proportion to compare the contribution each different value makes towards a total.

EXAMPLE

A survey was carried out amongst 60 people to find out their favourite type of music from a choice of three. The results are shown in the table below. Draw a pie chart to show the results.

Favourite type of Music	Frequency (No. of People)
Classical	15
Pop	25
Rock	20
	Total = 60

The first thing you have to do is to work out each group's value as a fraction of the whole (i.e. the total). To find the angle needed to draw that sector, you multiply the fraction by 360°.

Favourite type of Music	Frequency (No of People)	Fraction of each contribution	Angle to be drawn
Classical	15	$\frac{15}{60}$	$\frac{15}{60} \times 360° = 90°$
Pop	25	$\frac{25}{60}$	$\frac{25}{60} \times 360° = 150°$
Rock	20	$\frac{20}{60}$	$\frac{20}{60} \times 360° = 120°$
			Total = 360°

You can now draw your pie chart.

Pie Chart to show the most popular type of music.

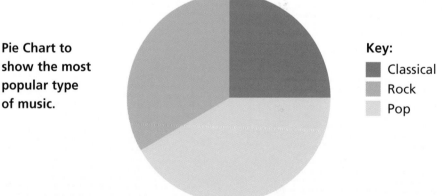

Key:
■ Classical
■ Rock
■ Pop

EXAMINER'S HINT:

After calculating the angles, always check your answers. To do this, just add all the angles together. You should get a total of 360° - if not, you need to go back and check your working.

EXAMINER'S HINT:

You must label your pie chart or use a key to show what each sector represents.

Make sure that your pie chart has an appropriate title.

TASK 4

1 ... A sports club has 180 members of whom 65 are adult males, 50 are adult females, 40 are young males and the remainder are young females. Draw a pie chart to show these proportions.

2 ... A group of people were asked to choose their favourite pizza from a choice of five. The results were as follows: Margherita 18, Four Seasons 24, Pepperoni 29, Vegetarian 6, Hawaiian 13. Draw a pie chart to show these results.

Scatter Diagrams

Scatter diagrams can show if there is a relationship between two sets of data. You plot each pair of values on the diagram, in a similar way to using map co-ordinates. If there is a **correlation** (i.e. relationship), you will be able to draw a **line of best fit**.

EXAMINER'S HINT:

You are expected to be able to draw conclusions from scatter diagrams using basic ideas of correlation.

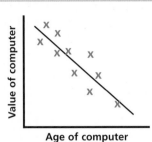

Positive Correlation	**Negative Correlation**	**No Correlation**
As the values in one set increase, so do the values in the other set.	As the values in one set increase, the values in the other set decrease.	There is no relationship between the two sets of values, so there is no line of best fit.

TASK 5

Draw a sketch of the scatter diagrams you would expect from the following data:
1. ... Number of miles travelled and the amount of petrol in the tank.
2. ... Length of hair and age.
3. ... Shoe size and height.

Line Graphs

Line graphs are used to show **continuous** data. They can also show more than one set of data so that comparisons can be made. The line graph here compares temperature readings taken at two-hour intervals on two consecutive days.

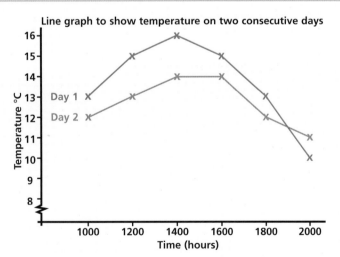

Line graph to show temperature on two consecutive days

EXAMINER'S HINT:

The points plotted on a line graph are joined using a line. This line can be used to provide approximate values for measurements that lie in between the plotted points.

For example, if you wanted to estimate the temperature at 1100hrs on Day 2...

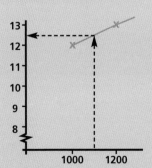

TASK 6

Bill and Jim weigh themselves once a month for a year.

Month	JAN	FEB	MAR	APR	MAY	JUN	JUL	AUG	SEPT	OCT	NOV	DEC
Bill's weight (kg)	81	80	80	79.5	80	80.5	81	82	81.5	80.5	80.5	81
Jim's weight (kg)	78	79	80.5	80.5	81	81.5	82.5	83	83.5	83	83	82.5

On the same axes, draw line graphs to show this data and then compare any fluctuations in Bill and Jim's weight throughout the year.

It is important to remember, these are only estimates - the line only shows the general pattern of change.

EXAMINER'S HINT:

Mean (or average) and range have already been covered at Level 1. Turn back to pages 26-27 to refresh your memory.

EXAMINER'S HINT:

In the test you may be expected to find the range or median of two sets of data and then compare them.

> You should be able to compare sets of data with a minimum of 20 items and use range to describe the spread within sets of data.

EXAMPLE

Calculate the mean, mode, median and range of the following set of data:

8, 7, 2, 10, 6, 7, 4, 9, 1, 6, 8, 4, 5, 4, 7, 7, 3, 9, 10, 2

Whenever you have to find the mode, median or range of a large data set, firstly arrange the values in size order, smallest to largest - this makes things much easier. The rearranged data would look like this:

1, 2, 2, 3, 4, 4, 4, 5, 6, 6, 7, 7, 7, 7, 8, 8, 9, 9, 10, 10

We can now calculate the mean, mode, median and range.

The **mean** or **average** of a set of data is given by...

> **MEAN** = $\dfrac{\text{TOTAL OF ALL THE VALUES}}{\text{NUMBER OF VALUES}}$

Using our data the **mean** = $\dfrac{119}{20}$ = **5.95**

The **mode** of a set of data is the value that occurs most often.

> **MODE = VALUE WHICH OCCURS MOST OFTEN**

Again, using our data, the **mode = 7** as this is the value that occurs the most often (4 times).

The **median** of a set of data is the middle value, when all the values have been arranged in order, smallest to largest.

> **MEDIAN = MIDDLE VALUE**

EXAMINER'S HINT:

When a data set has an even number of values, the median will always lie halfway between two values. If these two numbers are different, then you find their average - this is the median. However, when you have an odd number of values, the median will always be one of the values - the one that lies exactly in the middle.

Imagine the data arranged along a line. The exact middle of that line is halfway between the 10th and 11th value.

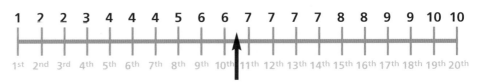

As you can see the 10th value is **6** and the 11th value is **7**. Halfway between 6 and 7 is **6.5**. This is the **median**.

The **range** is the difference between the largest and smallest value in a set of data.

> **RANGE = LARGEST VALUE – SMALLEST VALUE**

The largest value is 10 and the smallest value is 1.
This means that the **range = 10 – 1 = 9**

TASK 1

1 ... A survey was carried out on the shoe size of a group of 25 women. The results are shown below. Calculate the mean, mode, median and range of the results.

SHOE SIZE																								
6	7	7	5	8	9	4	6	8	6	5	8	5	6	7	7	6	4	6	5	6	5	9	6	7

2 ... The table below shows the results of an Internet search for the price of a particular camera. Calculate the mean, mode, median and range of the camera prices.

Camera	Cost (£)	Camera	Cost (£)	Camera	Cost (£)	Camera	Cost (£)
1	227	6	169	11	225	16	211
2	246	7	204	12	210	17	248
3	248	8	220	13	239	18	166
4	248	9	165	14	227	19	170
5	155	10	153	15	196	20	173

3 ... The table below shows the mean, mode, median and range of the High Street prices for the same camera. How do the High Street prices compare with the Internet prices?

MEAN	MODE	MEDIAN	RANGE
£231	£245	£225	£45

EXAMINER'S HINT:

At Level 2, you are expected to be able to compare sets of data and to use range to describe the spread within the sets. When you answer questions like this, take your time and always try to find a logical reason why there are differences in the mean, mode, median and range.

EXAMPLE
What percentage of the cameras found on the Internet (as shown above) cost less than £200?

Number of cameras less than £200 = 8
Number of cameras in total = 20
Therefore, percentage of cameras costing less than £200 = $\frac{8}{20}$ **x 100% = 40%**

EXAMINER'S HINT:

To revise percentages, refer pack to pages 12-13 and 33.

TASK 2

What percentage of the cameras found on the Internet (as shown above) cost...
1 ... more than £200?
2 ... less than £240?
3 ... more than £180 but less than £200?

You must be able to check your methods in ways that pick up faults and make sure your results make sense. You also need to know how to highlight the main points of your findings, describe your methods and explain how the results of the calculations meet the purpose of your activity.

Checking Your Work

It is essential that you check your work thoroughly, in both the test and your portfolio, to ensure it is accurate and makes sense.

EXAMPLE

The table below shows the amount of money collected by a small local charity from October to December, using collecting tins at three different locations.

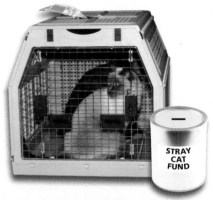

MONTH	LOCATION 1	LOCATION 2	LOCATION 3	TOTAL
October	28.08	16.73	18.23	63.04
November	32.96	21.01	18.16	72.13
December	26.12	19.57	16.03	61.72
TOTAL	87.16	57.31	52.42	**196.89**

To quickly check the overall total for sense, you can estimate an approximate answer.

$$28 + 17 + 18 + 33 + 21 + 18 + 26 + 20 + 16 = 197$$

EXAMINER'S HINT:

Remember, to calculate an estimate you simply round the numbers (see page 29).

If there is a big difference between your actual answer and the estimation, you will need to go back and check your calculations carefully. If your estimation is close to your actual answer, you should go on to check it for accuracy.

Remember to start with your answer and work backwards, reversing the maths. For this example, there are several ways of doing this. You could check the totals for each month (rows) or the totals for each location (columns). Finally, check the overall total.

$$63.04 + 72.13 + 61.72 = 196.89 \longrightarrow 196.89 - 61.72 - 72.13 = 63.04$$
$$87.16 + 57.13 + 52.42 = 196.89 \longrightarrow 196.89 - 52.42 - 57.31 = 87.16$$

EXAMINER'S HINT:

It is very important to clearly show your methods. This demonstrates your skills to the assessor and makes it easy for you to pick up any errors.

Checking your work is often a mental process, however, you must include some written evidence of these checks for the assessor's benefit.

TASK 1

Check the following calculations for both sense and accuracy, and make any necessary corrections.

1. ... $9.06 + 11.58 + 7.23 + 13.86 = 41.73$
2. ... $(3 \times 6.25) + 92 - 10 = 101.56$
3. ... $(£15.56 + £26.00 + £17.04) \div 2 = £117.20$

Presenting Your Findings

At Level 2, you have to undertake at least one 'substantial' activity for your portfolio. It should be broken down into three distinct parts:

> PLANNING → CALCULATING → PRESENTING

For your portfolio work to be a success, you need to clearly establish your aims at the planning stage. When it comes to presenting your findings and interpreting your results it is important that you keep these aims in mind.

Clearly shown methods and a well-chosen diagram can save you a lot of words. These can illustrate how you arrived at your answers and the main points in your findings far more effectively than a long narrative.

EXAMINER'S HINT:

Make sure the diagrams you use are appropriate to the type of data. Refer back to the section on diagrams (pages 51-53) if you are unsure.

EXAMPLE

Justin is going to buy a car. He decides to investigate which make and model within his budget is the best buy. He collects manufacturers catalogues and conducts a survey to get feedback from other drivers.

To present his findings he produces...
... a bar chart comparing the cost of the cars
... a table detailing the different cars' specifications
... a graph showing miles per gallon for each car at different speeds
... a pie chart showing the results of a survey about other driver's preferences

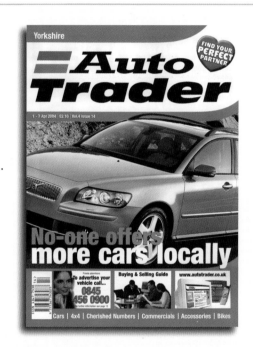

You will have to include some writing to explain the conclusions you have drawn from your findings. This needs to be clear and concise, describing how your findings meet your original aims. In Justin's case, he would specify which car he has decided to buy and explain how his findings led him to this decision. For example, the car he has chosen might be more economical to run than other cars of the same price and specification. It might also have come top in the survey showing other driver's preferences.

TASK 2

Suggest an appropriate way of presenting the following information:
1. ... Women's annual earnings compared to men's annual earnings in the same occupation.
2. ... The growth rate of two children over a 5 year period.
3. ... The proportion of members who use the different facilities available at the gym.

TASK 3

Turn back to the graphs and diagrams on pages 51 to 53. Practise explaining results, by writing a brief summary for each diagram, highlighting the key points of what it shows.

EXAMINER'S HINT:

If you have presented your findings effectively, you will only need to write a brief summary highlighting the key points.

You must show that you have developed skills in
- **Planning an activity and interpreting information**
- **Carrying out calculations**
- **Interpreting results and presenting your findings**

The symbols P and T indicate which skills are likely to be required for the portfolio and/or the test.

- Ⓟ ... Portfolio
- Ⓣ ... Test

Planning an Activity and Interpreting Information

In planning an activity and interpreting information you need to know how to...

- Ⓟ ... plan a substantial and complex activity by breaking it down into a series of tasks
- Ⓟ Ⓣ ... obtain relevant information from different sources, and use this to meet the purpose of your activity
- Ⓟ Ⓣ ... use estimation to help you plan, multiplying and dividing numbers of any size rounded to one significant figure
- Ⓟ ... make accurate and reliable observations over time and use suitable equipment to measure in a variety of appropriate units
- Ⓟ Ⓣ ... read and understand scale drawings, graphs, complex tables and charts
- Ⓟ Ⓣ ... read and understand ways of writing very large and very small numbers
- Ⓟ Ⓣ ... understand and use compound measures
- Ⓟ Ⓣ ... choose appropriate methods for obtaining the results you need and justify your choice

Carrying Out Calculations

In carrying out calculations you need to know how to...

- Ⓟ Ⓣ ... *show your methods clearly and work to appropriate levels of accuracy
- Ⓟ Ⓣ ... *carry out multi-stage calculations with numbers of any size
- Ⓟ Ⓣ ... use powers and roots
- Ⓟ Ⓣ ... work out missing angles and sides in right-angled triangles
- Ⓟ Ⓣ ... work out proportional change
- Ⓟ Ⓣ ... work out actual measurements from scale drawings and scale quantities up and down
- Ⓟ Ⓣ ... work with large data sets, using average and range to compare distributions, and estimate mean, median and range of grouped data
- Ⓟ Ⓣ ... rearrange and use formulae, equations and expressions
- Ⓟ Ⓣ ... *use checking procedures to identify errors in methods and results

Pythagoras of Samos (c.560 - c.480 BC)

Interpreting Results and Presenting Your Findings

In interpreting results and presenting your findings you need to know how to...

- Ⓟ Ⓣ ... select and use appropriate methods to illustrate findings, show trends and make comparisons
- Ⓟ Ⓣ ... examine critically, and justify, your choice of methods
- Ⓟ Ⓣ ... construct and label charts, graphs, diagrams and scale drawings
- Ⓟ Ⓣ ... draw appropriate conclusions based on your findings, including how possible sources of error might have affected your results
- Ⓟ Ⓣ ... explain how your results relate to the purpose of your activity

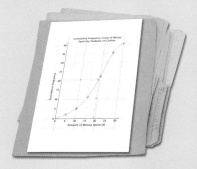

> You should be able to use estimation to help you plan, multiplying and dividing figures of any size rounded to one significant figure.

Rounding Numbers to One Significant Figure

EXAMINER'S HINT:

When using significant figures, you round the number in the same way as you learned at Level 1 (page 28).

Numbers can also be rounded to two, three or more significant figures e.g. 4 364 = 4 400 (2 s.f.), 4 364 = 4 360 (3 s.f.).

At Levels 1 and 2, you learned how to round numbers to the nearest ten, hundred, thousand etc. and to a given number of decimal places. At this level, you also need to be able to round numbers to one significant figure, so that the first digit is a non-zero (i.e. 1-9) and all the following digits are zeros.

EXAMPLES

34	⟶	30 to one significant figure (1 s.f.)
35	⟶	40 to one significant figure (1 s.f.)
627	⟶	600 to one significant figure (1 s.f.)
8 703	⟶	9 000 to one significant figure (1 s.f.)

TASK 1

Round the following numbers to one significant figure.

① 71 ② 99 ③ 555 ④ 44.44 ⑤ 1 009

Carrying Out Estimations

EXAMINER'S HINT:

When working with decimals, the first significant figure is the first digit that is not a zero e.g. 0.07680 is...

... 0.08 (1 s.f.)

... 0.077 (2 s.f.)

... 0.0768 (3 s.f.)

Carrying out estimations at the planning stage of an activity is very useful. It helps to provide an idea of what the final outcome might be. This means it is a good way of checking that your answers make sense.

EXAMPLES

A company records novels onto cassette tapes. The recording of a 376-page novel has a play time of 10 hours 40 minutes. The company reckons that 40 pages of the novel can be recorded onto a 60-minute tape. Use a method of estimation to check if this is likely.

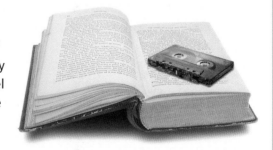

376 pages	⟶	400 pages (to 1 s.f.)
10 hours 40 minutes	⟶	11 hours (to the nearest hour)

So, if 400 pages have a play time of 11 hours, then...

The number of pages per hour $= \dfrac{400}{11} = 36.36 = 40$ (to 1 s.f.)

Therefore, the company's estimation was correct.

TASK 2

Use a method of estimation to check if the answers to the following calculations make sense.

① $7.5 \times 10.3 = 77$ ② $\dfrac{91 \times 561}{256} = 199$ ③ $\dfrac{(5.9)^2 + 13}{9.4} = 5.1$

You need to understand and know how to use compound measures.

Compound measures are used for quantities that cannot be measured directly, but can be expressed as a relationship between two other measurements. Speed, density and pressure are all compound measurements.

EXAMPLE

The tape in a standard 90-minute audio-cassette is 135 metres long. It takes 45 minutes to play one side of the tape. At what speed does the cassette play? Give your answer in centimetres per second.

EXAMINER'S HINT:

When you see a measurement given as 'something per something', it implies a division e.g. cm/s or g/cm³. When you see a measurement given as 'something - somethings', it implies a multiplication e.g. person-days.

Centimetres per second (cm/s) is a compound measure for speed. It means, 'the distance travelled (in centimetres) each second'. It also tells you how to calculate the measurement of speed. The formula is...

$$\text{Speed (cm/s)} = \frac{\text{Distance Travelled (cm)}}{\text{Time (s)}}$$

First, you need to convert the measurements you have been given into the appropriate units...

135 metres = 135 x 100cm = 13 500cm
45 minutes = 45 x 60 seconds = 2 700 seconds

Then you need to substitute these values into the formula to find the answer.

$$\text{Speed (cm/s)} = \frac{\text{Distance Travelled (cm)}}{\text{Time (s)}} = \frac{13\ 500}{2\ 700} = 5\text{cm/s}$$

EXAMINER'S HINT:

Square measurements (for area) and cubic measurements (for volume) are also compound measures. You need two (squared) or three (cubic) measurements to calculate them e.g.
square metres = m² = m x m
cubic metres = m³ = m x m x m

TASK 1

1 ... An object weighs 1.2kg. Its volume is 500cm³. Calculate its density in grams per centimetre cubed.

2 ... A marketing company hires some temporary members of staff to enter information into a database. The temping agency charges them by the person-day. If it takes 4 temps 21 working days to complete the task, how many person-days will the company be charged for in total?

> You need to know how to use powers and roots, and to read and understand ways of writing very large and very small numbers.

Understanding Powers

Powers show that a number is to be multiplied by itself a certain number of times.

4×4 $= 4^2$ (4 squared)
$4 \times 4 \times 4$ $= 4^3$ (4 cubed)
$4 \times 4 \times 4 \times 4 = 4^4$ (4 to the power 4) etc.

4^2 ← the power

Understanding Roots

You know that... $4^2 = 4 \times 4 = 16$

Another way of describing the relationship between 4 and 16 is to say 4 is the **square root** of 16. You can write 'the square root of 16' as $\sqrt{16}$ or $16^{\frac{1}{2}}$

Similarly, $\sqrt{25}$ or $25^{\frac{1}{2}} = 5$ (since $5 \times 5 = 25$)

You know that... $4^3 = 4 \times 4 \times 4 = 64$

4 is the **cube root** of 64. You can write 'the cube root of 64' as $\sqrt[3]{64}$ or $64^{\frac{1}{3}}$

Similarly, $\sqrt[3]{125}$ or $125^{\frac{1}{3}} = 5$ (since $5 \times 5 \times 5 = 125$)

Standard Form

If you are dealing with very large or very small numbers, it is not always practical to write them out in full each time. Likewise, if you are working with a calculator, the screen size will restrict the number of figures you can enter. **Standard form** is an alternative way of writing very large and very small numbers in shorthand.

To write a number in standard form, you move its decimal point a certain number of places so that it can be written as:

$$a \times 10^n$$

...where **a** must be a number that is equal to or greater than 1 and less than 10 and **n** is a positive or negative integer (i.e. a whole number).

EXAMPLES

... Very Large Numbers
$434 = 4.34 \times 10^2$
$362\,745 = 3.62745 \times 10^5$

... Very Small Numbers
$0.0434 = 4.34 \times 10^{-2}$
$0.00007168 = 7.168 \times 10^{-5}$

The process above is reversible and any number written in standard form can easily be written as a normal number.

TASK 1
Write the following numbers in standard form.

① 245   ② 87 426   ③ 0.0371   ④ 0.0001205

TASK 2
Write the following as 'normal' numbers.

① 8.73×10^2 ② 5.6×10^4 ③ 7.531×10^{-3} ④ 9.9×10^{-1}

EXAMPLE
Light from the sun takes just over 8 minutes to reach the earth, travelling at 186 000 miles per second. How far away is the sun? Give your answer in standard form.

8 minutes = 8 x 60 seconds = 480 seconds

Since light travels at 186 000 miles per second...

...the distance to the sun = **186 000 x 480 = 89 280 000 miles = 8.928 x 10⁷ miles**

EXAMINER'S HINT:

The 'standard form' button on most calculators is **EXP**.

When you enter a number in standard form you omit the **x10** e.g. 6.91×10^4 is entered into the calculator as **6.91 EXP 4**.

TASK 3
① ... A light year is the distance travelled by light in one earth year. Our nearest star, Alpha Centauri, is 4.3 light years away. How far away is Alpha Centauri in miles? Give your answer in standard form.

② ... In 1901 the population of England and Wales was 3.26×10^7. If the area of England and Wales is 151 000km² (to the nearest thousand), calculate the population per square kilometre.

③ ... In 2001 the population of England and Wales was 52.1 million. What was the increase in population from 1901 to 2001, as a percentage of the population in 1901?

④ ... A music company produces compilation CDs. Each CD has a 650 megabyte capacity, where 1 megabyte = 2^{20} bytes. What is the maximum number of complete songs that can be put on a single CD, if each song takes up 16 million bytes of storage?

EXAMINER'S HINT:

On most scientific calculators, there is a 'power' key x^y. To perform a calculation such as 4^3 you would enter **4 x^y 3 = 64**.

EXAMINER'S HINT:

Here is some basic algebra:

$2a = 2 \times a$

$ab = a \times b$

$abc = a \times b \times c$

$a^2 = a \times a$

$4a^2 = 4 \times a \times a$

$(4a)^2 = 4a \times 4a$

$4a + 3b = (4 \times a) + (3 \times b)$

$3a^2 + b = (3 \times a \times a) + b$

$4(2 + a) = 8 + 4a$

$2a(a - 3) = 2a^2 - 6a.$

Divisions and multiplications can be dealt with in any order. The same applies to additions and subtractions.

You will notice that the two examples involve all six operations. If you are unsure, always do one operation at a time in BODMAS order.

Try doing the operations in the two examples in the wrong order to see if you get a different answer - you should!

> **You must be able to rearrange and use formulae, equations and expressions.**

Algebra is a branch of mathematics where letters and other symbols are used to represent numbers and quantities in formulae, equations and expressions.

Substitutions

When you make substitutions into a formula that involves more than one operation, you must make them in the order shown here:

BODMAS

| **B**rackets | Powers **O**f | **D**ivisions and **M**ultiplications | **A**dditions and **S**ubtractions |

EXAMPLES

If **a** = 6, **b** = 10 and **c** = 12, calculate the value of...

1 $(a + b) + \dfrac{c}{2}$

$= (6 + 10) + \dfrac{12}{2}$

$= 16 + \dfrac{12}{2}$

$= 16 + 6$

$= 22$

2 $c^2 - 2ab$

$= 12^2 - 2 \times 6 \times 10$

$= 144 - 2 \times 6 \times 10$

$= 144 - 120$

$= 24$

TASK 1

If **a** = 4, **b** = 6 and **c** = -2, calculate the value of...

1 $a + b + c$ **2** $a^2 + bc$ **3** abc **4** $\dfrac{a + b}{c}$ **5** $\dfrac{ab^2}{c}$

Rearranging Formulae

EXAMINER'S HINT:

The two examples shown are formulae for finding **a** to begin with. We can say that **a** is the subject of the formula. When you rearrange formula, you are just making a different letter the subject.

There are many ways that a formula can be rearranged to change the subject. Don't worry if the method you use is different from the one shown here. As long as you get the correct answer, stick with it.

EXAMPLES

Rearrange the following formulae to make **b** the subject...

1 $a = 2b + 3$

(subtract 3 from both sides)

$a - 3 = 2b + 3 - 3$

(divide both sides by 2)

$\dfrac{a - 3}{2} = \dfrac{2b}{2}$

Therefore, $b = \dfrac{a - 3}{2}$

2 $a = \dfrac{b}{3} - 4$

(add 4 to both sides)

$a + 4 = \dfrac{b}{3} - 4 + 4$

(multiply both sides by 3)

$(a + 4) \times 3 = \dfrac{b}{3} \times 3$

Therefore, $b = 3(a + 4)$

TASK 2

Rearrange the following formulae to make **b** the subject:

1 $a = \dfrac{b}{2}$ **2** $a = \dfrac{b}{c}$ **3** $a = \dfrac{c}{b}$ **4** $2a + 3b = 4$

Simultaneous Equations

EXAMPLE

At break, a student buys 2 doughnuts and a coffee, which cost her 84p altogether. At lunchtime, the same student buys three doughnuts and two coffees, which cost 138p altogether. Form two equations with the information given and work out the individual price of a doughnut and a coffee.

If we use **d** to represent a doughnut and **c** to represent a coffee, we can form the following two equations:

At break: 2d + 1c = 84 (1)
At lunch: 3d + 2c = 138 (2)

We need both equations to contain the same number of 'd's or the same number of 'c's. To produce the same number of 'c's, we can multiply equation (1) by 2:

2d + 1c = 84 (1) x 2 ⟶ 4d + 2c = 168 (3)
3d + 2c = 138 (2) ⟶ 3d + 2c = 138 (2)

To remove the 'c's from the equations entirely, we now subtract equation (2) from equation (3).

```
   4d + 2c = 168
 – (3d + 2c = 138)
  ─────────────────
   1d      =  30
```
The cost of a doughnut is 30p.

Now we have a value for **d**, we can substitute it back into one of the equations to find the value of **c**. If we choose equation (1)...

2d + 1c = 84 (1)
2 x 30 + 1c = 84
1c = 84 – 60 = 24
The cost of a coffee is 24p.

EXAMINER'S HINT:

Simultaneous equations are where you work with two related equations (e.g. where **x** and **y** represent the same thing in both equations) at the same time. Individually the equations do not provide enough information for you to solve them (e.g. to find the value of **x** and **y**). However, when you work with both of them 'simultaneously', they provide enough combined information to solve them.

EXAMINER'S HINT:

When multiplying an equation, you must make sure that you multiply ALL the components by the same value.

In this example, to get the same number of 'd's we would have to multiply equation (1) by 3 and equation (2) by 2. Subtracting would remove the 'd's, so we could then work out the value of **c** etc. Both methods would give exactly the same values for **c** and **d**.

EXAMINER'S HINT:

To check your answers, substitute the value of **d** and **c** into equation (2).
3d + 2c
= (3 x 30) + (2 x 24)
= 90 + 48
= 138 (Which is correct!)

TASK 3

① ... Solve the following simultaneous equations and check your answers:
3a + b = 44 (1) 2a + 3b = 41 (2)

② ... The table below shows information about the total width taken up by combinations of standard and disabled parking bays in a car park.

Number of Standard Parking Bays	Number of Disabled Parking Bays	Total width
6	2	22.2m
3	3	18.3m

Form two equations from the information given and work out the widths of a single standard bay and a single disabled bay. Check your answers.

> You need to know how to work out proportional change.

Fractions, decimals and percentages can all be used to express proportion i.e. the size of a part in relation to the whole. Make sure you can convert between them confidently (page 33) and always be clear about what the whole is.

EXAMPLE

A local council recycled 12 000 tonnes of household waste in 2003. Its target is to increase this amount by an extra 5% year on year. Assuming the council achieves this target, how many complete years will it take to increase the weight of recycled waste to more than 14 500 tonnes a year.

EXAMINER'S HINT:

Finding a percentage is much quicker using the decimal form. It removes a whole step from the calculation.

The council needs to recycle 5% more compared to the previous year. If the previous year's total is always 100%, then the target for the year will be 105%.

$$105\% = \frac{105}{100} = 1.05$$

In other words, the amount recycled needs to go up by a multiple of 1.05 each year.

- **2004: Recycled Waste**
  = 1.05 x 12 000 tonnes = 12 600 tonnes
- **2005: Recycled Waste**
  = 1.05 x 12 600 tonnes = 13 230 tonnes
- **2006: Recycled Waste**
  = 1.05 x 13 230 tonnes = 13 891.5 tonnes
- **2007: Recycled Waste**
  = 1.05 x 13 891.5 tonnes = 14 586.075 tonnes

Therefore, it will take 4 years to achieve an annual turnover of more than 14 500 tonnes of recycled waste.

TASK 1

1 ... If the target increase for the council above had been 3% per year, how many complete years would it take the council to achieve an annual turnover of more than 14 500 tonnes of recycled waste?

2 ... Sue wants to invest £5 000 with her local bank for a period of 3 years. There are two ways in which she could invest her money:

- **Method A**: The same amount of interest is paid each year, calculated as 4% of the original investment sum.
- **Method B**: The interest paid each year is calculated as 3.8% of the total amount in the account at that time (i.e. original investment sum, plus interest earned in previous years).

Which method of investment should Sue choose? Support your answer with all the appropriate calculations.

EXAMPLE

Gnomes R Cool make 25 000 garden gnomes each year. The company wants to increase production by an extra 5% year on year. Use the following formula to calculate how many gnomes they will be making in 3 years time at this rate, to the nearest thousand.

Final Number of Gnomes = Initial Number of Gnomes $\left(1 + \dfrac{p}{100}\right)^t$

Where p = percentage increase and t = time in years.

If we use the formula, Final Number of Gnomes = $25\,000 \left(1 + \dfrac{5}{100}\right)^3$

$$= 25\,000 \times (1.05)^3$$
$$= 25\,000 \times 1.157625$$
$$= 28\,940.625$$
$$= \textbf{29\,000 (to nearest thousand)}$$

EXAMINER'S HINT:

To work out powers using a calculator, use the x^y key. To calculate $(1.05)^3$ enter **1.05** x^y **3** **=** .

If Gnomes R cool were to **decrease** production by 5% each year, then the formula would become:

$$\text{Final Number} = \text{Initial Number} \left(1 - \dfrac{p}{100}\right)^t$$

Check it out using the numbers in the example - you should get an answer of 21 000 gnomes (to the nearest thousand).

TASK 2

A new company sets up in competition with Gnomes R Cool. In the first year they only produce 20 000 gnomes, but they plan to increase production by 15% year on year. Use the formula above to calculate whether they will have overtaken Gnomes R Cool by the end of the 3 years.

EXAMPLE

Calculate the annual percentage increase in production the Gnomes R Cool would need to achieve if they were to produce 35 000 gnomes in the third year.

If we use the formula again, we are now trying to find the value of **p** …

$$35\,000 = 25\,000 \left(1 + \dfrac{p}{100}\right)^3$$

$$\dfrac{35\,000}{25\,000} = \left(1 + \dfrac{p}{100}\right)^3 \quad \text{(divide both sides by 25 000)}$$

$$\sqrt[3]{\dfrac{35\,000}{25\,000}} = \left(1 + \dfrac{p}{100}\right) \quad \text{(cube root both sides)}$$

$$1.12 = 1 + \dfrac{p}{100}$$

$$1.12 - 1 = \dfrac{p}{100} \quad \text{(subtract 1 from both sides)}$$

$$0.12 \times 100 = p \quad \text{(multiply both sides by 100)}$$

$$p = 12\%$$

Therefore, the company would need an annual increase in production of 12%.

EXAMINER'S HINT:

These calculations require you to rearrange a formula and great care is needed. If you have time in the test, you could always check your answer by substituting it back into the formula.

e.g. $25\,000 \left(1 + \dfrac{p}{100}\right)^3$

$$= 25\,000 \left(1 + \dfrac{12}{100}\right)^3$$
$$= 25\,000 \,(1.12)^3$$
$$= 25\,000 \times 1.40$$
$$= 35\,000 \text{ (which is correct!)}$$

TASK 3

What percentage increase per year would the council in the first example need to achieve if they wanted to recycle 16 000 tonnes of waste after 4 years?

You should be able to work out missing angles and sides in right-angled triangles from known sides and angles.

Pythagoras' Theorem

If you are given measurements for the length of two sides of a right-angled triangle, then the length of the third 'unknown' side can be calculated using **Pythagoras' Theorem**. The rule states that:

In a right-angled triangle, the square of the hypotenuse is equal to the sum of the squares of the other two sides.

This rule can be written as the formula:

$$(AB)^2 = (BC)^2 + (AC)^2$$

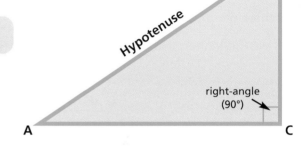

EXAMPLE

Calculate the length of the 'unknown' side in the triangle below using Pythagoras' Theorem.

This triangle is not drawn to scale

4cm
5cm

① Label your triangle (shown in black) making sure the hypotenuse is labelled AB
② The 'unknown' side is AB - the hypotenuse.
③ Now use Pythagoras' Theorem...

$$(AB)^2 = (BC)^2 + (AC)^2$$
$$= 4^2 + 5^2$$
$$= 16 + 25$$
$$(AB)^2 = 41$$

Think back to what you learned about powers and roots. If the hypotenuse squared, $(AB)^2$, is 41, then the hypotenuse is the square root of 41.

Therefore, AB = $\sqrt{41}$ = 6.4cm (to 2 s.f.)

TASK 1

Calculate the length of the 'unknown' sides in the following triangles using Pythagoras' Theorem (they are not drawn to scale). Give your answers to 2 significant figures.

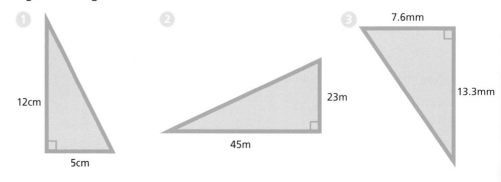

If the 'unknown' side in a right-angled triangle is one of the shorter sides, you can still use Pythagoras' Theorem to find its length. All you have to do is rearrange the formula.

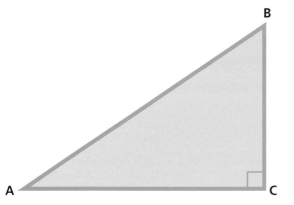

We know that...
$$(AB)^2 = (BC)^2 + (AC)^2$$

So, if you want to find the length of BC...
$$(BC)^2 = (AB)^2 - (AC)^2$$

And, if you want to find the length of AC...
$$(AC)^2 = (AB)^2 - (BC)^2$$

EXAMINER'S HINT:

A quick way to remember Pythagoras' Theorem is as follows:
- If you want to find the length of the **longest** side (i.e. the hypotenuse) square the other two lengths and **add** them together. You then need the square root to find your answer.
- If you want to find the length of one of the **shorter** sides (i.e. not the hypotenuse) square the other two lengths and **subtract** the smallest number from the bigger number. You then need the square root to find your answer.

EXAMPLE
Calculate the length of the 'unknown' side in the triangle below using Pythagoras' Theorem.

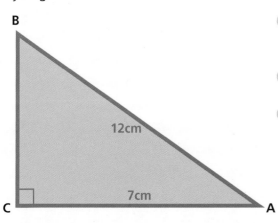

1. Label your triangle (shown in black) making sure the hypotenuse is labelled AB.
2. The 'unknown' side is BC - one of the shorter sides.
3. Now use Pythagoras' Theorem...

$$\begin{aligned}(BC)^2 &= (AB)^2 - (AC)^2 \\ &= 12^2 - 7^2 \\ &= 144 - 49 \\ (BC)^2 &= 95\end{aligned}$$

Therefore, BC = √95 = 9.7cm (to 2 s.f.)

TASK 2
Calculate the length of the 'unknown' sides in the triangles below using Pythagoras' Theorem (they are not drawn to scale). Give your answers to 2 significant figures.

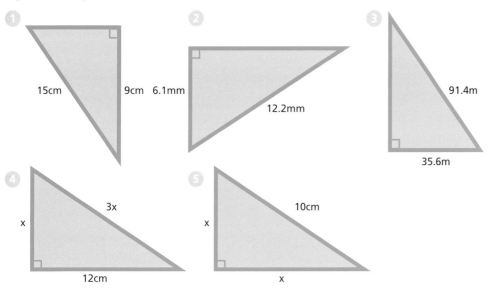

Trigonometric Ratios

Pythagoras' Theorem can only be used to calculate the length of an 'unknown' side when you have measurements for the other two sides. The three trigonometric ratios, **sin** (sine), **cos** (cosine) and **tan** (tangent), can also be used to calculate 'unknowns' in right-angled triangles. Each ratio involves one angle and two sides and they can be used to calculate unknown sides or unknown angles.

Before you begin, it is important that you can identify the different 'parts' of a right-angled triangle...

... θ is the angle you are working with i.e. have a value for or are trying to find a value for.

... The **Hypotenuse** (HYP) is the longest side and always opposite the right angle.

... The **Opposite** (OPP) is the side directly opposite θ.

... The **Adjacent** (ADJ) is the remaining side, next to θ.

EXAMINER'S HINT:

The acronym SOH CAH TOA (so-ka-toa) is commonly used to help remember these formulae. Like all formulae, they can be rearranged. Formula triangles are very useful when you are dealing with these ratios e.g. take the sin ratio, SOH...

To rearrange the formula to find the opposite (O), cover the 'O' in the triangle with your finger...

...to give OPP = sin θ x HYP.

To rearrange the formula to find the hypotenuse (H), cover the 'H' in the triangle with your finger...

... to give HYP = $\dfrac{\text{OPP}}{\sin \theta}$

You can do the same with the other two ratios. Make sure that you practise rearranging them.

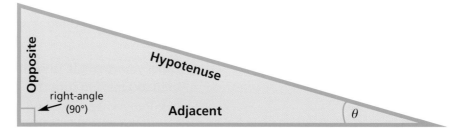

The three trigonometric ratios are:

$$\sin \theta = \frac{\text{OPP}}{\text{HYP}} \qquad \cos \theta = \frac{\text{ADJ}}{\text{HYP}} \qquad \tan \theta = \frac{\text{OPP}}{\text{ADJ}}$$

The formula you use (sin, cos or tan) will depend on the information you are given.

EXAMPLE

Calculate the length of AC in the triangle alongside.
Give your answer to 2 significant figures.

1. Label the sides (shown in black).
2. You want to calculate the ADJ and you know the HYP - use the **cos** ratio.
3. Rearrange using a formula triangle to give you...

   ADJ = cos θ x HYP

   = cos 65° x 10cm

   = 0.4226 x 10cm

   = 4.226

Therefore, length of AC = 4.2cm (2 s.f.)

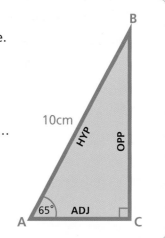

TASK 3

These triangles are not drawn to scale. Give your answers to 2 significant figures.

1. Calculate BC
2. Calculate BC
3. Calculate AB

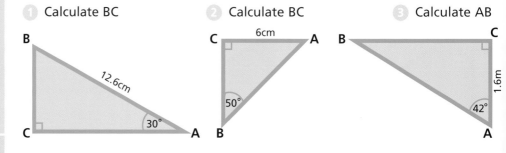

So far we have used the trigonometric ratios to calculate unknown sides. They can also be used to calculate unknown angles.

EXAMINER'S HINT:

These calculations do not involve rearranging the formula. However, the final stage of the calculation can be tricky, so great care is needed.

EXAMPLE

Calculate the size of angle $\theta(A\hat{B}C)$ in the following triangle, to one decimal place.

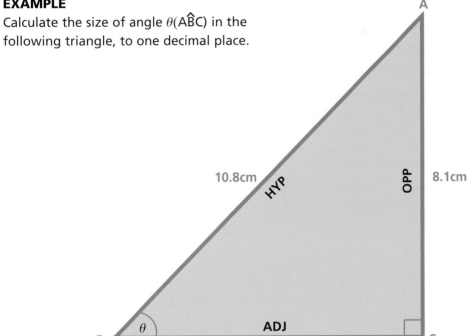

1. Label the sides (shown in black).
2. You want to calculate $\theta(A\hat{B}C)$ and you know the OPP and HYP - use the sin ratio.

$$\sin \theta = \frac{\text{OPP}}{\text{HYP}} = \frac{8.1}{10.8} = 0.75$$

3. This is NOT the final answer. What you now have is a value for **sin** θ and not θ. To find θ you need to use the sin^{-1} function (i.e. inverse sin) on your calculator.

Therefore $\theta = \textbf{sin}^{-1}\,\textbf{0.75}$
$$= \textbf{48.6}^{\circ}$$

EXAMINER'S HINT:

The sin^{-1}, cos^{-1} and tan^{-1} functions can be found above the sin, cos and tan keys on most calculators.

sin^{-1}	cos^{-1}	tan^{-1}
sin	cos	tan

To check your final answer, find the value of sin 48.6° using your calculator. You should get 0.75.

TASK 4

Calculate the value of θ for each of the following and check your answers.

1. $\sin \theta = 0.5$　　2. $\cos \theta = 0.5$　　3. $\tan \theta = 0.5$
4. $\sin \theta = 0.7432$　　5. $\cos \theta = 0.173$　　6. $\tan \theta = 2.6$

TASK 5

The triangles below are not drawn to scale. Give you answers to one decimal place.

1. Calculate $B\hat{A}C$　　2. Calculate $A\hat{B}C$　　3. Calculate $A\hat{B}C$

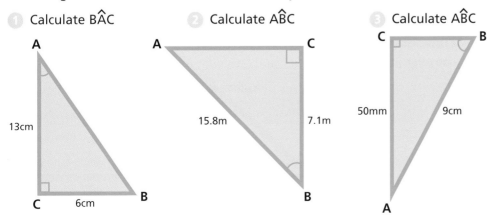

Having learned Pythagoras' Theorem and the rules of trigonometry, it is equally important that you can recognise when to use them. In the test, you will not be told how to calculate your answers. It is up to you to apply the appropriate number skills to a problem.

EXAMINER'S HINT:

Angles of Elevation are measured from the horizontal (in this case the ground) upwards.

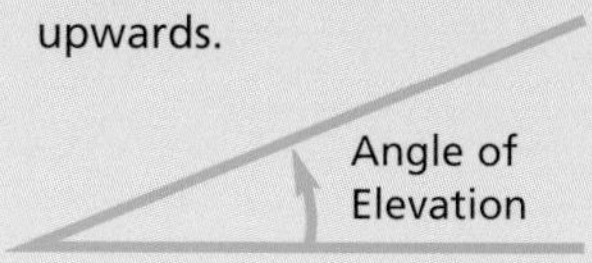

Angle of Elevation

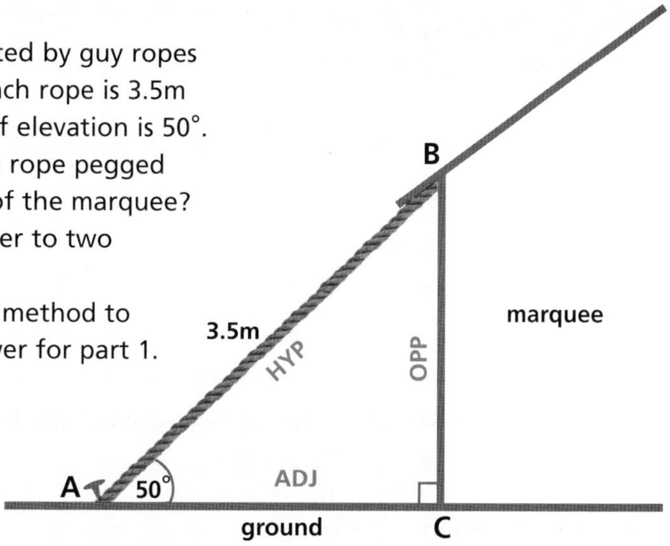

EXAMINER'S HINT:

Pythagoras' Theorem cannot be used here as there is only one known side.

EXAMINER'S HINT:

When you change the angle that you are working with, the OPP and ADJ change places too. The HYP never moves – it is always directly opposite the right angle.

EXAMPLE

A marquee is supported by guy ropes to keep it upright. Each rope is 3.5m long and the angle of elevation is 50°.

1 ... How far is each rope pegged from the foot of the marquee? Give your answer to two decimal places.

2 ... Use a different method to check you answer for part 1.

1 ... Label your triangle (shown in red). You know the **HYP** and are looking for the **ADJ**, so you need to use the **cos** ratio. Use the formula triangle to rearrange the equation to find ADJ...

ADJ = cos θ x **HYP**
    = cos 50° x 3.5
    = 0.6428 x 3.5
    = 2.25 (to 2 d.p.)
Each rope is pegged 2.25m from the foot of the marquee.

2 ... You need to use a different ratio to check your answer, so look closely at the information you have been given.

You know that the interior angles of a triangle add up to 180°, so angle AB̂C must be 40°. If you work with angle AB̂C, the side representing the distance from the rope to the foot of the marquee becomes the opposite (OPP). You now have the **HYP** and are looking for the **OPP**, so use the **sin** ratio (rearranged using the formula triangle).

OPP = sin θ x **HYP**
    = sin 40° x 3.5
    = 0.6428 x 3.5
    = 2.25 (to 2 d.p.)
This agrees with the answer in part 1.

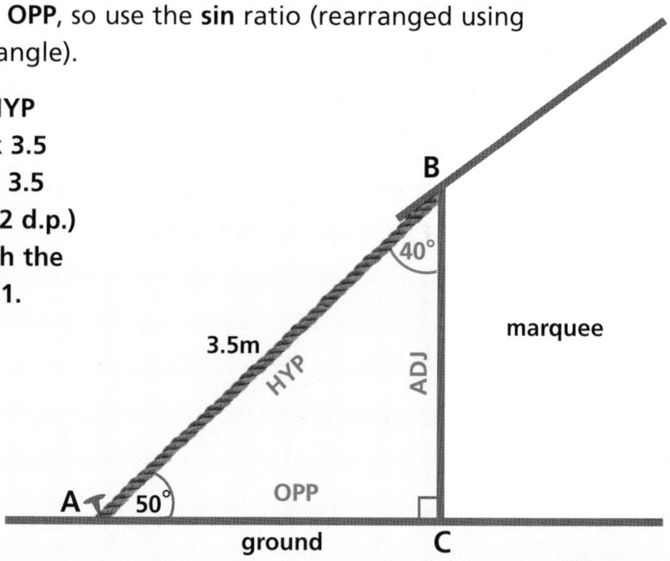

TASK 6

1 ... **a)** What is the height of the marquee's vertical wall (BC) in the example on the previous page?
b) Use a different method to check your answer for part **a)**.

2 ... When it is pitched, the sides of a tent are at 65° to the ground. Both sides are 200cm long.
a) How tall is the tent? Give your answer to the nearest 10cm.
b) Use a different method to check your answer for part **a)**.

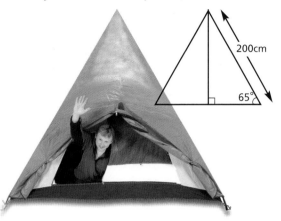

EXAMINER'S HINT:

All triangles can be split into two right-angled triangles e.g.

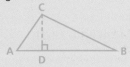

Triangles ACD and BCD are both right-angled triangles.

3 ... The diagram below shows the cross-section of the loft space in a house (the diagram is not to scale).
a) What is the height of the loft space at its tallest point?
b) Use a different method to check your answer for part a).
c) Work out the angle of elevation that roof panel AC makes with the base of the loft.
d) Use a different method to check your answer for part c).
e) Calculate the cross-sectional area of the loft space.

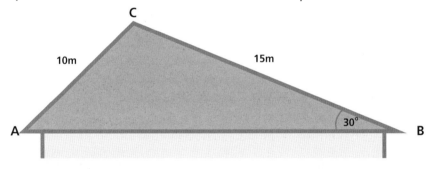

EXAMINER'S HINT:

Area of a triangle $= \frac{1}{2} \times$ base $\times$ height

4 ... The diagram below shows a wooden doorstop made from a triangular prism and a cuboid glued together (the diagram is not to scale).
a) Calculate the length of AC.
b) Use a different method to check part **a)**.
c) Calculate the length of BC.
d) Use a different method to check part **c)**.
e) Calculate the cross-sectional area of the doorstop.
f) The volume of the doorstop is 665cm³. Calculate the width of the doorstop to the nearest centimetre. Use the formula:
Volume = Area of Cross-section x Width

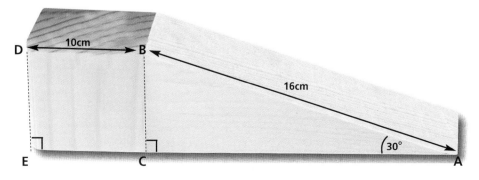

EXAMINER'S HINT:

A trapezium is a four-sided shape with just two parallel sides. Its area can be calculated by finding the average length of the two parallel sides and multiplying this average by the distance between the two sides.

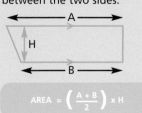

AREA $= \left(\frac{A+B}{2} \right) \times H$

> You need to be able to read, understand, construct and label scale drawings using accepted conventions, work out actual measurements from scale drawings and scale quantities up and down.

EXAMINER'S HINT:

You can use drawings of this type to scale objects up or down.

EXAMPLE

Scale 3:1

A clothing manufacturer has a logo, which appears on all their garments. It is a red rectangle with a white square enclosed in it. The diagram alongside shows the logo drawn to a scale of 3:1. Calculate the total area of the logo.

A scale of 3:1 means that 3 units of measurement in the drawing represents 1 unit of measurement in real life. In other words, the size of the 'object' in the drawing is bigger than the size of the actual 'object'.

Scale length of logo = 6cm   Actual length = $\frac{6cm}{3}$ = 2cm

Scale width of logo = 3cm   Actual width = $\frac{3cm}{3}$ = 1cm

Actual area of logo = length x width = 2cm x 1cm = 2cm²

EXAMINER'S HINT:

All the measurements you need to make a scale drawing are given on the sketch.

Use a sharp pencil and make your drawing as accurate as possible. This will help when you need to find the 'missing' measurements.

TASK 1

1 ... **a)** Calculate the actual area of the white square in the logo.
   b) What percentage of the logo is taken up by the white square?

2 ... The sketch below shows a plan view of a summer house.
   a) Draw a scale drawing of the summer house using a scale of 1:60.
   b) Calculate the area of the house floor in m².
   c) Calculate the area of the deck in m².
   d) What is the ratio of the area of the summer house floor to the area of the deck?

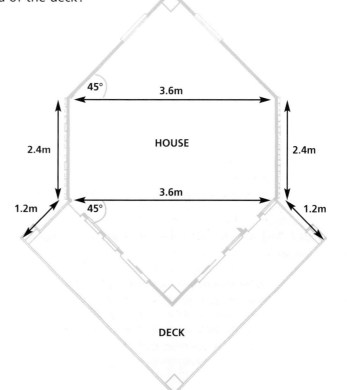

Below are scale drawings of two plots of land. Plot B has twice the length and width of Plot A.

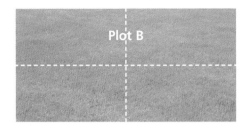

You should notice that the area of Plot B is FOUR TIMES bigger than the area of Plot A, even though the corresponding measurements of length and width are only TWO TIMES bigger. This is always the case.

If the dimensions of a particular area are doubled then the area will quadruple. If they triple then the area will increase ninefold.

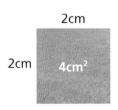

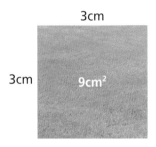

EXAMINER'S HINT:

- The units of length are cm, m, km etc.
- The units of area are cm², m², km² etc.

This is why we **square** the ratio of the corresponding dimensions to find the ratio of the corresponding areas.

TASK 2

1 ... Two neighbours, Mr Regan and Mr Carter, both want to build conservatories at the back of their houses. Scale drawings of both conservatories are shown below. They are each drawn to a scale of 1:100.

a) Calculate the area of each conservatory's floor space in m².
b) What is the ratio of the area of Mr Regan's conservatory to Mr Carter's conservatory?
c) What is the ratio of the corresponding dimensions of Mr Regan's conservatory to Mr Carter's conservatory?
d) Use a suitable method to check that your answers to parts **b)** and **c)** make sense.

2 ... An object weighs 12 grams. Calculate the weight of a replica object, if its dimensions are all increased in the ratio 1:3.

3 ... The surface area of an object and a replica are 20cm² and 80cm² respectively.
a) Calculate the ratio of their corresponding dimensions.
b) If the smaller object weighs 50g, calculate the weight of its replica.

EXAMINER'S HINT:

If the length, width and breadth of an object are increased in the same ratio, its volume and weight will increase, in the following way:

Ratio of DIMENSIONS	Ratio of corresponding VOLUMES
1:2	(1:2)³ = 1:8
1:3	(1:3)³ = 1:27
1:4	(1:4)³ = 1:64

The units of volume are cm³, m³, km³ etc. This is why we cube the ratio of corresponding dimensions to find the value of corresponding volumes.

EXAMINER'S HINT:

Do not expect tables to always appear as a simple grid. They can take lots of different formats.

You must be able to read and understand complex tables.

You must be able to identify the data within a complex table that is relevant to your calculations. Have a look at the tables below. They contain all the information you need to answer the task questions.

TASK 1

1 ... Jenny plans to make biscuits to sell at the summer fair. The table below shows the ratio and cost of the ingredients needed.

Ingredient	Ratio	Cost
Butter	8	79p/250g
Caster Sugar	4	82p/1kg
Plain Flour	13	40p/1.5kg

A batch of 20 biscuits uses a total of 500g of raw ingredients. If Jenny wants to make 8 batches...

a) ... how many grams each of butter, sugar and flour does she need?

b) ... what is the total cost of the ingredients she must buy, if they are only available from the shop in the quantities shown above?

c) ... how many grams of each ingredient will be left over from the total bought?

d) ... how much profit will she make if each biscuit is sold for 12 pence?

e) ... what is this profit as a percentage of the cost of ingredients?

2 ... Below is a homeowner's electricity bill for one quarter.

METER READING AND CHARGES

Reading Dates	latest	previous	units	cost	charges
15 Nov - 15 Feb	18685	17365	1320	5.940p	£78.41
Standing Charge					
Up to 14 Feb		92 days at 9.39p per day			£8.64
Total Charges					£87.05
VAT @ 5.0%					£4.35
Amount Due					£91.40

a) If the billing period is 92 days, what is the mean number of electricity units used each day?

b) If the homeowner continues to use electricity at the same rate, how many units of electricity will he use in one year?

c) If the charges remain the same, how much money can the homeowner expect to pay on electricity in one year, including standing charges and VAT?

d) Calculate the standing charges for one year as a percentage of the total cost for one year?

3 ... The table below shows the cost of calls as they appear on a phone bill.

COST OF CALLS			£23.595
Type of Call	Total Nº of Calls	Total Duration	Total Cost
Local	84	04:39:24	£5.532
National	60	03:22:44	£9.610
To a mobile	44	03:11:24	£7.579
Directory enquiry	2	00:02:28	£0.721
Other Calls	1	00:01:45	£0.153

a) Calculate the different rates that the bill payer is being charged for local, national and 'to a mobile' calls in pence per second.

b) What is the mean duration of local calls in seconds?

c) What is the total cost of calls to mobile phones as a percentage of the total call charges?

d) A third of all the local calls are made to friends and family. If she subscribes to a special offer by the phone company, the bill payer can save 10% on these calls. Use the mean call duration (calculated in part b) to calculate an estimate of how much money this would save.

4 ... The table below shows how to break down your earnings and calculate the income tax and National Insurance contributions payable on each sum.

Income Tax

Breakdown of Gross Earnings	Tax Payable
First £4 615	0%
£4 616 - £6 575	10%
£6 576 - £35 115	22%
£35 116 +	40%

National Insurance

Breakdown of Gross Earnings	National Insurance Contribution
First £4 615	0%
£4 616 - £30 940	11%
£30 941 +	1%

Carol receives an annual salary of £9 000.

a) Calculate the total amount of income tax Carol will have to pay in 1 year.

b) Calculate the total amount Carol will have to pay in National Insurance contributions in a year.

c) How much money will Carol receive each year after these deductions?

d) What is this amount as a percentage of her gross earnings?

EXAMINER'S HINT:

Your 'gross earnings' are the total amount of money you are paid before any deductions are made.

> You should be able to read, understand, construct and label charts, graphs and diagrams using accepted conventions. You also need to be able to select and use appropriate methods to illustrate findings, show trends and make comparisons.

Basic Charts, Graphs and Diagrams

Pie Chart
Used to show proportion i.e. the contribution each value makes to a total.

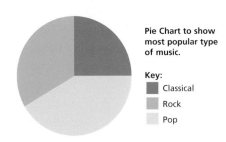

Pie Chart to show most popular type of music.

Key:
- Classical
- Rock
- Pop

Bar Chart
Used to display discrete data. Can also be used to compare two or more sets of data.

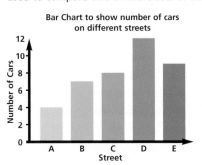

Histogram
Used to display grouped continuous data.

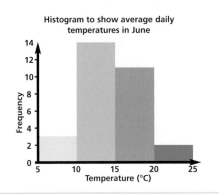

Line Graphs
Used to display continuous data. Can also be used to show more than one set of data.

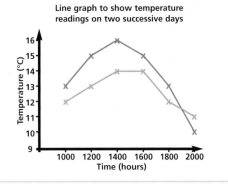

TASK 1

① ... Two friends, one in Glasgow and one in Manchester, record the temperature every hour for a 12-hour period starting at 8am. All temperatures were measured to the nearest degree Celsius. Present the data below in the most suitable way. Give reasons to support your choice.

Glasgow	6	8	9	11	11	10	9	9	7	7	6	5
Manchester	10	11	11	12	11	13	12	11	11	8	7	7

② ... A motorist keeps a record of the time it takes him to drive to work each day over a 12-week period. The table below shows the times in minutes, to the nearest minute. Present this data in the most suitable way. Give reasons to support your choice.

50	53	49	51	49	56	63	47	52	52	48	53	36	61	52	43	59	54	61	49
65	41	45	56	36	39	40	50	55	42	45	51	50	43	50	48	52	44	52	44
45	51	58	47	52	57	42	51	53	38	50	52	47	50	37	25	48	54	54	49

Scatter Diagrams

Scatter diagrams (or graphs) can be used to show whether there is a correlation (i.e. relationship) between two sets of values. If there is a correlation, a line of 'best fit' can be drawn.

EXAMINER'S HINT:

To revise the basics of scatter diagrams, turn back to page 53.

EXAMPLE

Ten students take a Maths and English test. The results are as follows:

Student	1	2	3	4	5	6	7	8	9	10
Maths Test Result	35	27	48	20	54	34	22	44	28	54
English Test Result	48	27	63	18	89	53	28	72	42	82

a) Draw a scatter diagram, including a line of best fit, to show if there is a correlation between the Maths results and English results.
b) Describe the relationship between the two sets of results?
c) Another student scored 45 in her Maths test but was absent for the English test. Use your scatter diagram to estimate her result in the English test.

a)

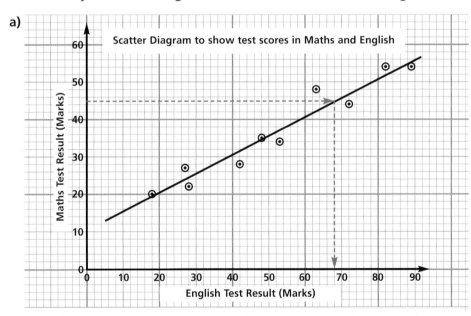

EXAMINER'S HINT:

There are many ways of plotting the points on a scatter diagram e.g. **X**, ⊙, and ● are common.

b) Students who gained high marks in their Maths tests also gained high marks in their English test. Students who got poor marks, did so in both subjects. This is an example of **Positive Correlation**.
c) Based upon this correlation, you would expect a student who scored 45 in Maths to score 68 in English (see diagram above).

TASK 2

The number of kilometres driven and amount of petrol left in a previously full tank after 10 different journeys are given in the table.

Number of kilometres driven	240	480	260	350	530	180	420	420	320	470
Petrol left in tank (litres)	23	8	22	19	6	29	13	11	17	7

a) Draw a scatter diagram, including a line of best fit, to show the information in the table.
b) Use your graph to work out the estimated number of kilometres driven if there is 16 litres of petrol left in a previously full tank.

> You should be able to work with large data sets (over 50 items) using measures of average and range to compare distributions, and estimate the mean, median and range of grouped data.

Finding the mean, median, mode and range of sets of data has already been covered at Levels 1 and 2 (see pages 26-27 and 54-55). At this level, you need to be able to work with very large data sets and grouped data.

EXAMPLE

Calculate the mean, median, mode and range of the following data, which gives the total amount of money (in pounds) spent on clothes each month by a group of students.

Amount of Money Spent (£)	Frequency	'Middle' Amount of Money Spent (£)	Frequency x 'Middle' Amount of Money Spent (£)
1-5	2	3	2 x 3 = 6
6-10	3	8	3 x 8 = 24
11-15	6	13	6 x 13 = 78
16-20	11	18	11 x 18 = 198
21-25	13	23	13 x 23 = 299
26-30	5	28	5 x 28 = 140
	TOTAL = 40		TOTAL = £745

EXAMINER'S HINT:

You can only estimate the mean value for grouped data because you do not know the exact values.

To calculate **the mean** (or average) amount of money spent, we need to add two further columns to our frequency table. These are shown highlighted.

① **'Middle' Amount of Money Spent**
Each row in this column shows the 'middle' amount of money spent e.g. for the class interval 1-5, the 'middle' amount spent is £3.

② **Frequency x 'Middle' Amount of Money Spent**
Each row in this column gives an approximation of the total amount of money spent for that class interval, using the 'middle' amount of money as representative of that class e.g. in the first row **2** students spend **£3** to give a total of **£6**.

The mean is calculated using the following formula:

$$\text{Mean} = \frac{\text{Total of All the Values}}{\text{Number of Values}}$$

This can be modified to suit the frequency table shown above:

$$\text{Mean} = \frac{\text{Total for 'Frequency x 'Middle' Amount of Money Spent' Column}}{\text{Total for 'Frequency' Column}}$$

$$= \frac{£745}{40}$$

$$= £18.63$$

$$= £19 \text{ (to the nearest £)}$$

EXAMINER'S HINT:

All the amounts in the frequency table are given to the nearest pound (£). Your answer should be given to the same level of accuracy.

We can estimate that the mean amount of money spent by the students is **£19**.

The **median** is the middle value of a set of data. When the data is grouped, as it is in the table on the facing page, we need to plot a cumulative frequency curve to find this value. To calculate cumulative frequency you add each frequency to all those preceding it.

EXAMINER'S HINT:

We can easily work out that the median is between £16 and £20, because this is the class interval where the 20th and 21st values occur. However, to get a more accurate value we have to draw a cumulative frequency curve.

Amount of Money Spent (£)	Frequency
1-5	2
6-10	3
11-15	6
16-20	11
21-25	13
26-30	5
	TOTAL = 40

Amount of Money Spent (£)	Cumulative Frequency
5 or less	2
10 or less	5 (2+3)
15 or less	11 (2+3+6)
20 or less	22 (2+3+6+11)
25 or less	35 (2+3+6+11+13)
30 or less	40 (2+3+6+11+13+5)
	TOTAL = 40

You can now plot a graph.

As there are 40 values (i.e. students) in total, the median is between the 20th and 21st value.

The graph shows that the median is **£19.50**.

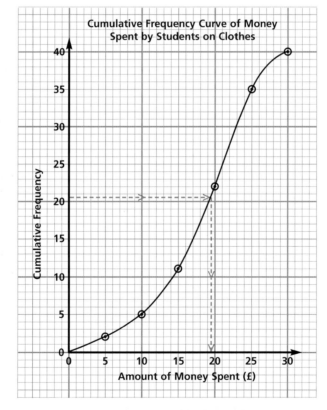

EXAMINER'S HINT:

When plotting a cumulative frequency graph, make sure you connect the points with a smooth, curved line. It will normally form an 's' shaped curve.

The **mode** is the value that occurs most often in a set of data. When the data is grouped, you do not know the individual values but, you can find the **modal class** i.e. the class interval with the highest frequency. Therefore, the modal amount of money spent is **£21-£25**.

The **range** is the largest value minus the smallest value in a set of data. When class intervals are used to record data, we assume that the data is spread across each class interval i.e. there are values at the bottom, middle and top of the class. The lowest class interval is 1-5, giving us the smallest value: **1**. The highest class interval is 26-30, giving us the largest value: **30**. Therefore, range = £30 - £1 = **£29**.

EXAMINER'S HINT:

When lots of data is included in the lowest and highest class interval, the calculation of range is fairly accurate.

TASK 1

1 ... This table gives the recorded midday temperature everyday for June.

a) Calculate the mean recorded temperature.
b) Calculate the median recorded temperature by drawing a cumulative frequency curve.
c) What is the modal recorded temperature?
d) What is the range of the recorded temperatures?

Temperature T (°C)	Frequency
5≤T<10	3
10≤T<15	14
15≤T<20	11
20≤T<25	2

2 ... This table shows the number of hours worked by the employees of a company each week.

Number of Hours Worked		
Not less than	Up to	Number of Employees
10	15	2
15	20	3
20	25	8
25	30	18
30	35	21
35	40	8

a) Calculate the mean, median (by drawing a cumulative frequency curve), mode and range of the number of hours worked.
b) The managers of the company are reviewing the number of hours worked by their employees. Which value - the mean, median, mode or range - is of most use to them? Explain your answer.

3 ... This histogram shows the waiting times for a group of passengers at a bus stop.

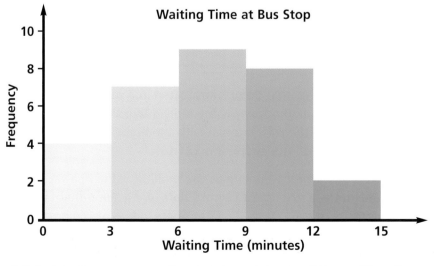

a) Calculate the mean, median, mode and range of the waiting times.
b) What fraction of the passengers have to wait for 9 minutes or more?

Histograms with Unequal Column Widths

EXAMPLE

This table shows the distribution in the weight of 50 people who attend an aerobics class at the local gym. Draw a histogram to illustrate this data.

Weight of people in kg (W)	Frequency	Frequency Density
40<W≤50	4	4
50<W≤60	10	10
60<W≤70	24	24
70<W≤90	12	$\frac{12}{2} = 6$

EXAMINER'S HINT:

The class interval 40<W≤50, means that the weight recorded is more than 40kg, but less than or equal to 50kg.

Two Important Points:

1 ... The area of each column in a histogram is proportional to the frequency of the class interval that it represents. The first three class intervals in our data represent 10 kilograms, whilst the 4th (70<W≤90) represents 20 kilograms. It is twice the size of the others, which means that the width of this column in our histogram will be twice the width of the other columns. Remember, **area = height x width** so, if the area of the column is proportional to the frequency and we have doubled the width, we will have to halve the height to ensure the area stays the same.

2 ... The quantity plotted on the y axis is now called **frequency density**, as shown highlighted in the table above.

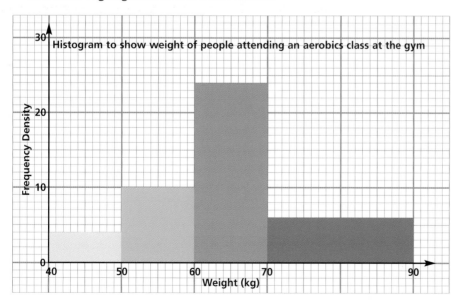

TASK 2

This table shows the distribution in the height of 80 individuals. Draw a histogram to illustrate this data.

Height in cm (H)	140<H≤150	150<H≤160	160<H≤180	180<H≤210
Frequency	9	37	28	6

PLANNING A SUBSTANTIAL ACTIVITY

> You need to know how to plan a substantial and complex activity by breaking it down into a series of tasks. You should be able to obtain relevant information from different sources, including a large data set (over 50 items), and use this to meet the purpose of your activity, make accurate and reliable observations over time and use suitable equipment to measure in a variety of appropriate units.

Don't be put off by the words 'complex' and 'substantial'. This simply means that you need to produce a fairly large-scale piece of work, which can be broken down into a series of smaller, more manageable tasks, that demonstrate a whole range of number skills. The success of portfolio work is dependent upon preparing a clear plan of action.

EXAMINER'S HINT:

People don't plan to fail, they fail to plan! Don't start any portfolio work until you are absolutely clear about what has to be done.

EXAMINER'S HINT:

It makes sense to choose an activity you find interesting or useful. You could start with a special interest you have, or a task that you have to complete for work or college. If you do this, you are less likely to lose enthusiasm.

The first step is to come up with an idea for your activity. For example, if you are interested in getting fit, you might decide to base your work around that topic.

Once you have formulated an idea, you need to develop it. You need to be more specific about what you want to achieve and make sure you have a definite **aim** or **purpose**.

For this example, a suitable aim might be to formulate a diet and exercise regime that will enable you to achieve and sustain a healthy weight and level of fitness.

Talk through your ideas with your friends, colleagues and tutor, to get a clear picture of what you are going to do and how you are going to do it.

All complex and substantial activities should follow the same basic structure:

1 Planning and Collecting Information
2 Carrying Out Calculations
3 Presenting and Interpreting Findings

With this in mind, carefully plan everything you need to do to achieve your aim. Start by asking yourself the following questions…

1 … What information and data do I need to collect?
2 … Where will I find it / How will I gather it?
3 … What will be the best way of organising this data?
4 … How will it help me achieve my purpose / What kind of analysis will I need to carry out?

There may not be a straightforward answer to these questions. Indeed, they may raise even more questions.

Flow charts can be a useful planning tool, helping you to identify all the subtasks you will need to complete to achieve your aim.

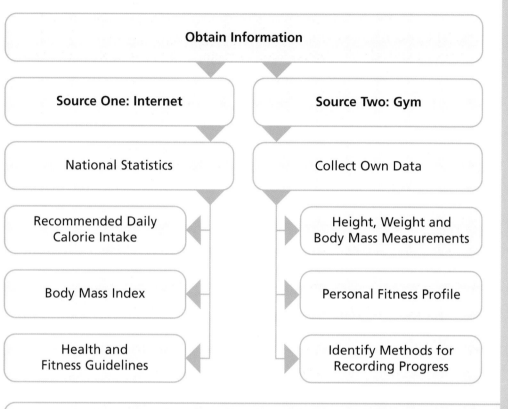

EXAMINER'S HINT:

When planning your activity, it is important to be practical. Bear in mind the resources that are available to you and don't set yourself unrealistic tasks.

The number skills that you have developed at Level 3 fall into four main categories. The work in your portfolio needs to demonstrate your abilities in all of these areas:

Amounts and Sizes
You need to show that you can use powers, roots and standard form correctly, and can find missing angles and sides in right-angled triangles.

Scales and Proportion
You should demonstrate that you can use scale and proportion to change quantities, as well as understanding the implications of such calculations.

Handling Statistics
You must show that you can use various methods to compare and explore sets of data.

Rearranging and Using Formulae
You need to demonstrate that you can use formulae and simultaneous equations, rearranging them to change the outcome where required.

If it is appropriate to your purpose, you should try to include calculations from at least two of these areas in your substantial activity.

EXAMINER'S HINT:

Produce a clear, one-page plan for your activity to show your tutor. Make sure you have their agreement before continuing further, you don't want to generate lots of unnecessary work.

TASK 1
One of Edith's colleagues told her that it could be cheaper to import a new car from Europe than buy it in the UK. She decides to investigate this claim and see if it is true.

1. ... Help Edith to plan her project, by answering the four questions opposite.
2. ... Draw a flow chart showing all the tasks that Edith needs to complete before she can begin making calculations.

EXAMINER'S HINT:

When it comes to collecting information for your activity, you must make sure it is **relevant** and **accurate**. Re-read the section about obtaining relevant information at Level 2 (pages 46 - 49). If you are collecting you own data, it is important that you use equipment and units of measurement appropriate to the task.

> You should be able to select appropriate methods for obtaining the results you need, examine critically, and justify, your choice of methods. You need to draw appropriate conclusions based on your findings, including how possible sources of error might have affected your results, and explain how your results relate to the purpose of your activity.

At Level 3, it is not enough just to display your findings in a suitable and attractive way. You must be able to draw appropriate conclusions and evaluate your work critically and honestly.

Imagine you had to carry out the same activity all over again. Would you approach it differently? How could you improve your work? What would you change?

EXAMINER'S HINT:

When drawing your conclusions, it is vital that you refer back to your original aims.

EXAMPLE

Simon used information from various Internet sources to devise a diet plan and exercise regime. His aim was to achieve and sustain a healthy weight and fitness level.

He followed the diet plan and exercise regime for 24 weeks. Every two weeks, he took his measurements and completed a set of controlled tests to record his progress in the following three areas: stamina, aerobic fitness and body weight. The results were plotted in line graphs.

The line graph below shows Simon's weight measurements in kg, taken over the 24-week period, compared to the recommended maximum and minimum weights for someone of his height.

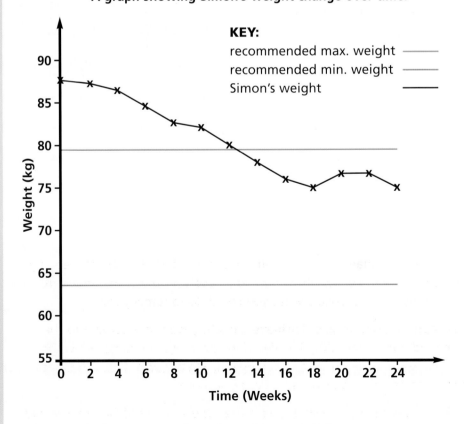

A graph showing Simon's weight change over time.

What conclusions can you draw from these results?

Justifying Your Methods

It is important that you can justify the method you have chosen for presenting your findings.

Simon chose a line graph to show his weight measurements over the 24 week period. The data is continuous, so it was an appropriate choice. It illustrates the pattern of change (i.e. the downward trend) effectively and allows him to make a clear comparison between his own weight and the maximum and minimum recommended weights for someone of his height.

TASK 1

① ... Name another method that can be used for presenting continuous data.

② ... Would this method have been more or less effective than a line graph for showing Simon's weight data? Explain your answer.

EXAMINER'S HINT:

Turn back to pages 22-25 and 51-53 to remind yourself of the advantages and disadvantages of different types of chart, graph and diagram for presenting data.

Identifying Sources of Error

You must be aware of possible sources of error and inaccuracy in your work. You should also be able to suggest ways in which they could be reduced.

Simon would need to consider the following factors, amongst others:
- The recommended weights on the Internet do not take into account body shape or distinguish between body fat and muscle.
- The accuracy of his measurements will depend on the precision of the scales he was using and the level of accuracy of his readings.
- More frequent readings would have made the line graph more accurate.

TASK 2

① ... To measure his stamina, Simon recorded the distance he could run (in km) on a treadmill in 12 minutes. He performed the same test every two weeks. Name three factors that might affect the accuracy of his data?

② ... Suggest what steps Simon should have taken to ensure that his data was as accurate as possible.

EXAMINER'S HINT:

When collecting your own data, try to minimise inaccuracies by using the same equipment each time.

Always state the level of accuracy you are working to e.g. to the nearest gram.

Explaining Your Results

When it comes to explaining your results, ask yourself: do my results meet my original aim? If the answer is yes, you need to explain how. If the answer is no, explain why not and discuss what you could do to remedy this.

Simon's graph shows that he did **achieve** a healthy weight according to the recommended guidelines, using his diet plan and exercise regime. However, it does not show whether or not he successfully **sustained** it. To do this, data would need to be collected over a longer period of time.

Obviously, to draw any conclusions about the fitness aspect of Simon's original aim, you would need to look at all his other methods and findings (e.g. for stamina and aerobic fitness).

EXAMINER'S HINT:

In your conclusions, remember to include any ideas you might have for further work, leading on from your findings.

Multiplication Square

1	2	3	4	5	6	7	8	9	10
2	4	6	8	10	12	14	16	18	20
3	6	9	12	15	18	21	24	27	30
4	8	12	16	20	24	28	32	36	40
5	10	15	20	25	30	35	40	45	50
6	12	18	24	30	36	42	48	54	60
7	14	21	28	35	42	49	56	63	70
8	16	24	32	40	48	56	64	72	80
9	18	27	36	45	54	63	72	81	90
10	20	30	40	50	60	70	80	90	100

Conversion Tables

METRIC → IMPERIAL

LENGTH

METRIC		IMPERIAL
1 millimetre (mm)		0.0394in
1 centimetre (cm)	10mm	0.3937in
1 metre (m)	100cm	3.2810ft
1 kilometre (km)	1000m	0.6214 mile

VOLUME/CAPACITY

METRIC		IMPERIAL
1 millilitre (ml)		0.0018pt
1 centilitre (cl)	10ml	0.0176pt
1 litre (l)	1 000ml	1.7600pt

MASS (WEIGHT)

METRIC		IMPERIAL
1 milligram (mg)		
1 gram (g)	1 000mg	0.0353oz
1 kilogram (kg)	1 000g	2.2046lb
1 tonne (t)	1 000kg	0.9842 ton

IMPERIAL → METRIC

LENGTH

IMPERIAL		METRIC
1 inch (in)		2.5400cm
1 foot (ft)	12in	0.3048m
1 yard (yd)	3ft	0.9144m
1 mile	1760yd	1.6090km

VOLUME/CAPACITY

IMPERIAL		METRIC
1 fluid ounce (fl.oz)		28.4130ml
1 pint (pt)	20fl.oz	0.5683 litres
1 gallon (gal)	8pt	4.5460 litres

MASS (WEIGHT)

IMPERIAL		METRIC
1 ounce (oz)		28.3500g
1 pound (lb)	16oz	0.4536kg
1 stone	14lb	6.3503kg
1 hundredweight (cwt)	8 stone	50.8020kg
1 long ton	20cwt	1.0160t

EXAMINER'S HINT:

To convert a temperature from...

...Fahrenheit (°F) to Celsius (°C):

$C = \frac{5}{9}(F - 32)$

...Celsius (°C) to Fahrenheit (°F):

$F = \frac{9}{5}C + 32$

Shapes

RECTANGLE

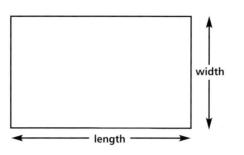

Area = Length x Width

CUBOID

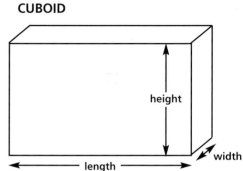

Volume = Length x Width x Height

PARALLELOGRAM

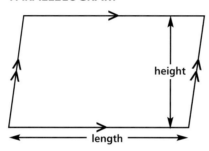

Area = Length x Height

PRISMS

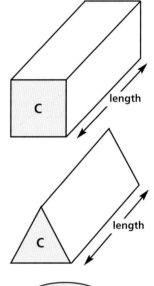

Volume = $\dfrac{\text{Area of Cross-section (C)}}{}$ x Length

TRAPEZIUM

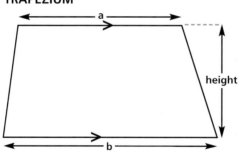

Area = $\dfrac{(a + b)}{2}$ x Height

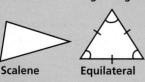
TRIANGLE

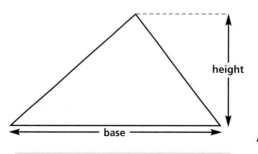

Area = $\dfrac{1}{2}$ Base x Height

PYRAMID / CONE

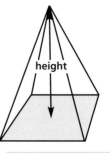
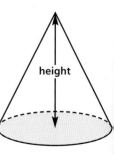

Volume = $\dfrac{1}{3}$ Area of Base x Height

Shapes (cont)

CIRCLE

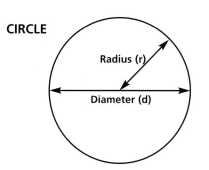

SPHERE

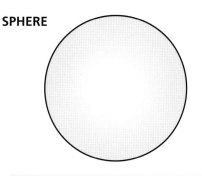

EXAMINER'S HINT:

In a circle...

Circumference = $2\pi r$ or πd

Radius (r) = $\frac{d}{2}$

AREA = πr^2 or $3r^2$

Volume = $\frac{4}{3}\pi r^3$

Pythagoras' Theorem

$(AB)^2 = (BC)^2 + (AC)^2$

A

Hypotenuse

right-angle
(90°)

C

B

Trigonometric Ratios

$\sin \theta = \dfrac{OPP}{HYP}$

$\cos \theta = \dfrac{ADJ}{HYP}$

$\tan \theta = \dfrac{OPP}{ADJ}$

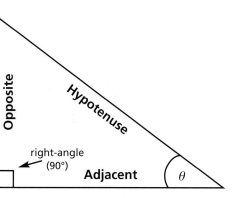

Opposite

Hypotenuse

right-angle
(90°) **Adjacent** θ

Mean, Mode, Median and Range

MEAN = $\dfrac{\text{TOTAL OF ALL THE VALUES}}{\text{NUMBER OF VALUES}}$

MODE = VALUE WHICH OCCURS MOST OFTEN

MEDIAN = MIDDLE VALUE

RANGE = LARGEST VALUE – SMALLEST VALUE

EXAMINER'S HINT:

To estimate a mean for grouped data you use the same equation. To find the **Total of All the Values** you need to find the total for each class interval first (multiply the frequency by the 'middle' value) and add them all together. To find the **Number of Values** simply add all the frequencies together (see page 54).

Key Skills: Communication
- Available NOW - £4.50

Key Skills: Information Technology
- Available NOW - £5.50 including CD-ROM

Written by specialists who are currently involved in the delivery and assessment of Key Skills, these guides present all the required skills in a concise and user-friendly format.

Besides being a brilliant resource for students they also provide a framework for teachers who may be unfamiliar with the QCA specifications for the Key/Basic Skills areas.

Collectively, the Key Skills guides provide comprehensive coverage of Levels 1-3, and students studying Basic Skills can use Communication Levels 1 and 2 to prepare for the tests in Adult Literacy.